GREAT BOOK OF
WHODUNITS

D1508991

 Sterling Publishing Company, Inc.
New York

10 9 8 7 6 5 4 3 2 1

Published in 2001 by Sterling Publishing Company, Inc.
387 Park Avenue South, New York, N.Y. 10016

Material in this collection was adapted from

Five-Minute Whodunits
© Stan Smith

Sherlock Holmes'
Puzzles of Deduction
© Tom Bullimore

Inspector Forsooth's Whodunits
© Derrick Niederman
and

Five-Minute Crimebusters
Clever Mini-Mysteries
© Stan Smith

Distributed in Canada by Sterling Publishing
c/o Canadian Manda Group
One Atlantic Avenue, Suite 105
Toronto, Ontario, Canada M6K 3E7

Distributed in Great Britain and Europe by Cassell PLC
Wellington House, 125 Strand
London WC2R 0BB, United Kingdom

Distributed in Australia by Capricorn Link (Australia) Pty Ltd.
P.O. Box 6651, Baulkham Hills, Business Centre
NSW 2153, Australia

Sterling ISBN 0-8069-8507-0

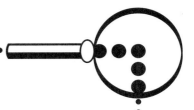

CONTENTS

Five-Minute Whodunits

Sherlock Holmes' Puzzles of Deduction

Inspector Forsooth's Whodunits

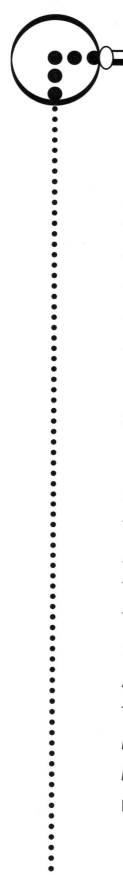

Five-Minute Crimebusters

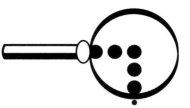

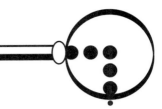

FIVE-MINUTE WHODUNITS

STAN SMITH

ILLUSTRATED BY LUCY CORVINO

MR. THOMAS P. STANWICK

EVEN THOSE UNACQUAINTED with Thomas P. Stanwick are often struck by his appearance. A lean and lanky young man, he stands six feet two inches tall. His long, thin face is complemented by a full head of brown hair and a droopy mustache. Though not husky in build, he is surprisingly strong and enjoys ruggedly good health.

His origins and early life are obscure. He is undeniably well educated, however, for he graduated with high honors from Dartmouth College as a philosophy major and studied logic and history at Cambridge University for a year or two afterwards. He now lives alone (with a pet Labrador) in a bungalow in the New England town of Baskerville, not far from the city of Royston. His house is filled with books, chess sets, maps, and charts. He earns a living as a freelance editor of textbooks on geometry and American history.

Personally, Stanwick is good-humored and amiable. His relaxed manner conceals the strength of his convictions and the intensity of his intellectual interests. He enjoys the company of his many friends, but cherishes his personal freedom and independence. The regular patterns of his life suit him well, and the pursuit of wealth, fame, or power holds no attraction for him.

His main interests are his intellectual pursuits. First and foremost, he is a logician, particularly skilled in traditional formal deduction. As an incessant student of its theoretical and practical aspects, he is fascinated by all sorts of mysteries and puzzles. Aside from pure logic, other

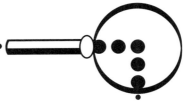

interests of his include philosophy, chess, history, music, mathematics, literature, and etymology. An avid bibliophile, he owns hundreds of books on those topics.

Stanwick's personal tastes are simple. He is a casual dresser, and almost never wears a tie. His eating preferences are old-fashioned and include beef and potatoes. An ardent Anglophile, he has several British habits acquired during his many long stays in England. He prefers tea to coffee, for example, and smokes a pipe.

Besides seeing his friends, Stanwick's favorite pastimes are reading and chess. He is also fond of hiking in the New England hills. He takes long travel vacations in the summertime and often visits England. Sometimes he stays with the Earl of Stanwyck, a distant relative, at the earl's East Anglian estate or at his country estate in Scotland. He also enjoys visiting London and Cambridge, where he has many friends from his student days. Back home in Baskerville, he carries on an active correspondence.

He spends many of his evenings conversing with friends at the Royston Chess Club and elsewhere. When he has a hand in investigating and solving crimes, it is usually through his friendship with Inspector Matt Walker, a promising detective on the Royston police force who is about five years older than Stanwick. They play chess together at the chess club on Thursday evenings, and Stanwick occasionally drops by police headquarters.

Stanwick's interest in criminal cases is purely that of a logician. In that capacity, as Walker would be the first to admit, he is frequently very useful.

A MERE MATTER OF DEDUCTION

THOMAS P. STANWICK, the amateur logician, removed a pile of papers from the extra chair and sat down. His friend Inspector Matthew Walker had just returned to his office from the interrogation room, and Stanwick thought he looked unusually weary.

"I'm glad you dropped by, Tom," said Walker. "We have a difficult case on hand. Several thousand dollars' worth of jewelry was stolen from Hoffman's Jewel Palace yesterday morning. From some clues at the scene and a few handy tips, we have it narrowed down to three suspects: Addington, Burke, and Chatham. We know that at least one of them was involved, and possibly more than one."

"Burke has been suspected in several other cases, hasn't he?" asked Stanwick as he filled his pipe.

"Yes, he has," Walker replied, "but we haven't been able to nail him yet. The other two are small potatoes, so what we really want to know is whether Burke was involved in this one."

"What have you learned about the three of them?"

"Not too much. Addington and Burke were definitely here in the city yesterday. Chatham may not have been. Addington never works alone, and carries a snub-nosed revolver. Chatham always uses an accomplice, and he was seen lurking in the area last week. He also refuses to work with Addington, who he says once set him up."

"Quite a ragamuffin crew!" Stanwick laughed. "Based on what you've said, it's not too hard to deduce whether Burke was involved."

Was Burke involved or not?

Solution on page 22

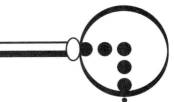

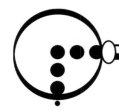

A QUIET MORNING AT THE OFFICE

"THERE CAN BE NO question of suicide," stated Cooper emphatically. "The murder weapon, a handgun with a silencer, was found immediately in front of the victim's desk, but beyond where he could have dropped it. It also had no fingerprints, and he wasn't wearing gloves."

"I agree," said Walker. "The gun, of course, was photographed and taken for evidence before we removed the body."

Inspector Matthew Walker of the Royston Police Department, Thomas P. Stanwick, and FBI Special Agent Ryan Cooper were in the inner office of Wilson Jasper. Until he had been found shot at his desk a few hours earlier, Jasper had been a vice president of Supertech Corporation.

The reliable Sergeant Hatch entered the office and reported to Walker.

"As you can see, sir," he said, "there are only four doors out of this office. Three lead to the offices of Jasper's aides: Joseph Springer, John King, and William Farrar. Their offices also open onto the outer hallway. The fourth door, directly facing the desk, leads to the outer office, which is occupied by Ms. Pringle, Jasper's secretary, and two clerks. The windows behind Jasper's desk cannot be opened."

While listening to Hatch's report, Stanwick glanced again over the large, bloodstained desk. When he and Walker had arrived, the body had still been slumped over the blotter, which was covered with several spattered piles of financial reports, performance evaluations, and other papers. Also on the desk were a telephone console, a pen set, a calendar, a family photograph, and a few knickknacks. A personal computer rested on a side table beside the chair.

"I've finished questioning the aides," Hatch continued. "Springer said he didn't see Jasper this morning. Jasper didn't send for him, and Springer said he didn't want to disturb him while he was doing evaluations. King and Farrar also denied seeing him this morning. Neither

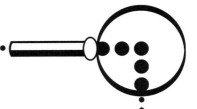

was sent for, and Farrar was busy with quarterly reports."

"How about Ms. Pringle?" asked Walker.

"She says Jasper arrived about eight, went right into his office, and closed the door. He had a full briefcase with him, as usual. He cleaned off his desk each night and brought a caseful of papers home."

"Did he have any appointments this morning?" asked Cooper.

"None that she knew of, and no one appeared for one. He kept his schedule and to-do list to himself. In a nutshell, no one saw anyone enter or leave Jasper's office except Jasper himself, and no one heard a shot or a noise. Ms. Pringle found the body when he wouldn't answer his intercom for a call."

"Well," said Cooper with a sigh, "a Bureau team will soon be here to examine the offices more thoroughly. It may tie in with one of our current investigations. Certainly we have established that access to the inner office was exceedingly limited."

"I think we have established rather more than that," Stanwick remarked.

"Such as?"

"Such as the identity of the killer," said Stanwick quietly.

Who murdered Wilson Jasper?

Solution on page 22

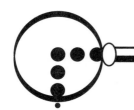

A STAMP OF SUSPICION

THOMAS P. STANWICK and Inspector Matthew Walker were chatting in the lounge of the Royston Chess Club after an arduous game.

"Any interesting cases on hand, Matt?" asked Stanwick, lighting his pipe.

Walker nodded. "A robbery case involving a stamp collector. What's driving me nuts is that I think the victim may be lying, but I can't prove it."

"Really?" Stanwick arched his eyebrows. "Please tell me about it."

"It happened, supposedly, three nights ago, in one of the mansions up on the Hill," Walker said. "The owner, Avery Manlich, says that he was awakened about 2 A.M. by a noise downstairs in his library. Grasping a baseball bat, he crept down the stairs and paused there to switch on the light to the foyer. He also called out "Who's there?" in the direction of the library.

"To his astonishment, two men darted out of the library and ran out the front door into the night. By the time the shocked Manlich rushed to the open door, the men were gone. Only then did he go back to the library and find his safe cracked and at least ten trays of valuable stamps missing."

"Just a moment," interrupted Stanwick. "While he was at the door, did he hear any car doors slamming or an engine starting?"

"No, he didn't. The thieves escaped on foot."

"Did Manlich describe the thieves?"

"Nothing very helpful. He said the men were dressed only in black, skintight leotards, black gloves, and black ski masks. As they ran out, both had their arms full of several trays of stamps."

"And what did your investigation reveal?"

"The deadbolt lock on the front door had been sawed off, the other lock on that door had been picked, and the safe (a rather sophisticated one) had been expertly cracked. No fingerprints or other physical evidence was left, and according to Manlich, nothing but the stamps was taken. The stamps were heavily insured, of course. Neither on the grounds nor in the surrounding area have we found any discarded ski

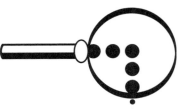

masks or other traces of the thieves."

"And on what basis do you doubt Manlich's story?"

Walker made a wry face.

"Not much more than a gut feeling, I guess," he said. "I've dealt with collectors before though, Tom. Though usually normal in all other respects, they tend to be fanatical when it comes to their collections. This guy Manlich, it seems to me, has been just a little too cool about this whole thing. Of course, it's nothing I could take to court."

"No, I suppose not," said Stanwick with a smile. "I think a more solid basis can be found, however, for your suspicions about Manlich. His story does contain a major flaw!"

What flaw did Stanwick detect in Manlich's story?

Solution on page 22

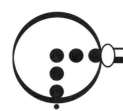

THE CASE OF
THE DUBIOUS DROWNING

"A DROWNING AT DUNCOMB residence, 857 Whippoorwill Drive. Victim middle-aged woman. Ambulance and unit en route."

Inspector Matt Walker and Thomas P. Stanwick listened intently to the terse announcement on Walker's police radio. Whippoorwill Drive was only minutes away, so without a word, Walker, who was giving Stanwick a ride home, turned his car toward it.

The ambulance and a police car arrived just before them. Walker and Stanwick followed the commotion to the swimming pool, about 60 feet in back of the formidable Duncomb mansion. The emergency crew had just pulled Marjorie Duncomb from the pool and was trying to revive her. A moment later they hoisted her, still dripping in her swimsuit, onto a stretcher and rushed her to the ambulance.

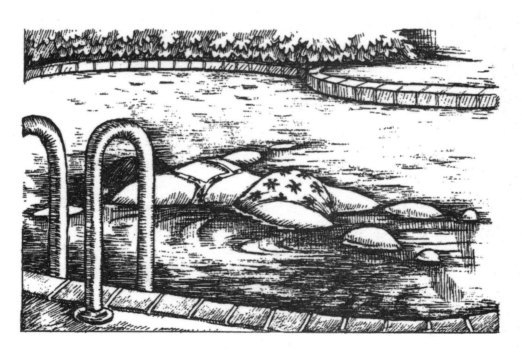

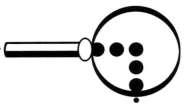

"No life signs, sir," one medical technician said to Walker as he hurried past. Walker turned to the two police officers and a disheveled, graying man standing by the pool.

"Mr. Duncomb?" he asked, flashing his badge. "Did you call this in?"

"Yes," replied the disheveled man, still staring toward the departing ambulance. "I found Marjorie face-down in the pool. The poor dear must have had a heart attack during her swim and drowned."

"Were you looking for her?"

"Yes. I knew she was late getting back from her swim. It was after three."

"Did she swim every day, then?"

"That's right. Even now, in October. It's getting chilly, though, so we were going to close up the pool for the season next week. Only next week!"

Stanwick glanced around. The pool was well maintained, but the furnishings were few: three lounge chairs and a small table. A pair of sandals lay beside one of the chairs, and a book and a pair of sunglasses lay on the table.

"Did your wife have a weak heart, Mr. Duncomb?" asked Stanwick.

"Just a bit of angina, but she took medication for it. Poor dear!"

"Matt," said Stanwick quietly, drawing Walker aside. "If Mrs. Duncomb cannot be revived, will an autopsy be required?"

"Of course."

"Well, I think you will find little or no water in her lungs. This is wrong. She didn't drown. She died elsewhere and was moved to the pool, which indicates murder. Until the autopsy results are in, I think you had better keep an eye on the husband."

Why does Stanwick suspect that Mrs. Duncomb was murdered?

Solution on page 23

STANWICK AND THE SPURIOUS SILVER MINER

"AND HOW CAN I help you, Mr. ... Lancaster?"

"Lanchester, Garver Lanchester. Just up from southern Brazil, and delighted to be visiting New England."

Thomas P. Stanwick, the amateur logician, lit his curved briar and looked curiously at the visitor seated in the opposite armchair whose unexpected appearance had interrupted his research into ancient geometrical studies. Lanchester, a large mustachioed man, wore a trace of an Australian accent and, despite the February cold, the light khakis of an explorer.

"Inspector Walker has given me a letter of introduction," Lanchester said, handing Stanwick a sealed envelope. "He told me you had some millions to invest, despite your modest lifestyle, as he put it, sir."

Stanwick froze in astonishment for a second before taking and opening the envelope. Inside he found a slip of paper with a few lines of Walker's distinctive handwriting:

> Sorry to tell fibs about you, Tom, but I thought you'd find Mr. Lanchester's story as interesting as I did.
>
> Matt

"Please proceed, Mr. Lanchester," said Stanwick, leaning back in his chair and smiling expectantly.

"Well, sir," Lanchester began, "I've spent the better part of my life prospecting for precious metals in some of the more remote areas of the world. China, Mongolia, northern Canada, Siberia, the jungles of Southeast Asia, as well as the outback of my native Australia, have all felt the mark of my pick and shovel.

"Five weeks ago, I found myself in the hill country of southern Brazil, just north of Porte Alegre. I had heard legends of old silver mines in that area. Well, by Gawd, sir, they were true! A cluster of caves I

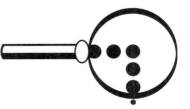

discovered there show strong signs of rich deposits of silver. I've filed the proper papers with the Brazilian authorities. My next step is to organize a team to excavate the mines properly.

"That's where I need investors like yourself, sir. We'll need fuel, jeeps, mining equipment, tents, food—enough for several weeks. If the mines are deep enough, I can set up a permanent organization."

"And if you find the investors you need, how soon do you propose to return to the mines?"

"Immediately, sir!"

"Hadn't you better wait until summer?"

"No sir, I'm ready to start now!"

Stanwick laughed heartily. "I'm afraid I can't help you, Mr. Lanchester, or whatever your name really is. My hidden millions are as much a fantasy as your Brazilian silver mines, as Matt Walker is well aware. Begone now, sir!"

Why doesn't Stanwick believe his visitor's story?

Solution on page 23

19

A THEFT AT THE ART MUSEUM

THE THEFT OF SEVERAL valuable paintings from the Royston Art Museum created a sensation throughout New England. Two days after Stanwick's return from a visit to Scotland, he was visited by Inspector Matt Walker, who was in charge of the case. As Stanwick poured tea, Walker quickly brought his friend up to date on the case.

"We've identified the gang of five thieves who must have done this job," Walker reported. "Archie McOrr, who never finished high school, is married to another one of the five, Charlayne Trumbull. The other three are Beverly Cuttle, Ed Browning, and Douglas Stephens."

"I thought you told me earlier that only four people were involved in the robbery," said Stanwick.

"That's right. One stayed in the car as the driver, another waited outside and acted as lookout, and two others entered the museum and carried out the actual theft. One of the five gang members was not involved in this particular job at all."

"And the question, I hope," said Stanwick with a smile, "is who played what part, if any, in the theft."

"Exactly." Walker flipped open his notebook. "Though I'm glad to say that our investigation is already bearing some fruit. For example, we have good reason to believe that the lookout has a Ph.D. in art history, and that the driver was first arrested less than two years ago."

"A remarkable combination," Stanwick chuckled.

"Yes, indeed. One of the actual thieves (who entered the museum) is the sister of Ed Browning. The other thief is either Archie or his wife."

"What else do you have on Douglas?"

"Not much. Although he's never learned to drive, he used to be a security guard at the Metropolitan Museum of Art in New York."

"Interesting. Please go on."

"The rest is mainly odds and ends." Walker thumbed through a few more pages of notes. "Charlayne, an only child, is very talented on

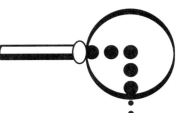

the saxophone. Beverly and Ed both have criminal records stretching back a decade or more. We've also learned that the driver has a brother who is not a member of the gang."

"Most interesting indeed," remarked Stanwick. He handed Walker a mug of tea and sat down with his own. "Your investigation has made excellent progress. So much, in fact, that you already have enough to tell who the thieves, the lookout, and the driver are."

Who are they?

Solution on page 23

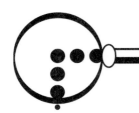

SOLUTIONS

A Mere Matter of Deduction (page 10)

At least one of the three is guilty. No others were involved. If Burke is guilty, then of course he was involved. If Addington is guilty, then he must have had an accomplice (since he never works alone), but it couldn't have been Chatham, who refuses to work with him, so it must have been Burke.

Similarly, if Chatham is guilty, then he must have had an accomplice, who couldn't have been Addington, with whom he refuses to work, and so must have been Burke.

Therefore Burke must have been involved in the case.

A Quiet Morning at the Office (page 12)

Jasper had cleaned off his desk the previous night, unpacked his papers only after arriving that morning, and kept his work schedule to himself. Once shot, he had slumped over his papers. Only someone who had seen him at his desk before he was shot could have known what he was working on.

Springer, however, had referred to Jasper's working on performance evaluations. He could have known this only by seeing the papers on Jasper's desk that morning before the shooting. Springer had therefore lied about not seeing Jasper that morning before the shooting, which only the killer would have had reason to do.

A Stamp of Suspicion (page 14)

A deadbolt lock had been sawed off, a door lockpicked, and a sophisticated safe cracked. What then became of the saw, the lockpick, and the safe-cracking tools?

No tools were left in the study, or carried in the thieves' arms, or hidden on their persons (the leotards were skintight), or taken to an escape car. If Manlich's story were true, the thieves would have had to do the work with their bare hands, which was absurd.

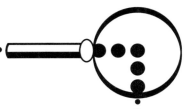

The Case of the Dubious Drowning (page 16)

Stanwick observed that there was no towel or robe by the pool. Not even a hardy swimmer would normally choose to walk 60 feet from an outside pool to a house in increasingly chilly weather dripping wet. He therefore deduced that the swimming incident had been staged, and suspected—correctly, as it turned out—Mr. Duncomb.

Stanwick and the Spurious Silver Miner (page 18)

In the southern hemisphere, January and February are summer months. Stanwick's visitor is plainly unaware of this, which would be an impossibility if he had just visited southern Brazil.

A Theft at the Art Museum (page 20)

One of the thieves is Ed's sister, who cannot be Charlayne, an only child, and must therefore be Beverly. The other thief is either Archie or Charlayne, his wife. Douglas, who was on the scene, is neither one of the thieves nor the driver (since he can't drive), so he must be the lookout.

Ed is neither one of the thieves nor the lookout. With his long criminal record, he can't be the driver, who was first arrested less than two years ago. He is therefore the one not involved.

Charlayne, an only child, cannot be the driver, who has a brother. She must therefore be one of the thieves, and her husband Archie must be the driver.

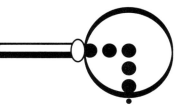

SHERLOCK HOLMES'
PUZZLES OF DEDUCTION

TOM BULLIMORE

ILLUSTRATED BY
IAN ANDERSON

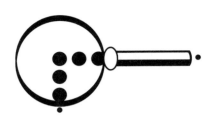

PUZZLE 1

"Take a look at this, Watson," said Holmes as he passed a coded message to his colleague.

The message read:

> TO SHERLOCK HOLMES,
>
> T5M5RR5W4W4LLST32LTH3CR5WN
>
> J3W3LSTH4SW4LLB3MYGR32T3STTR46MPH.
>
> MORIARTY

"What does it all mean, Holmes?" exclaimed Watson.

"To find that out, Watson, we must break the code. The numbers obviously represent letters."

"But he doesn't use the numbers one or zero, Holmes," said Watson.

"That is simply because they could be mistaken for the letters I and O, Watson," said Holmes as he set about breaking the code.

Can you decipher the message?

Solution on page 87

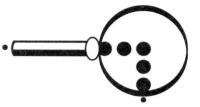

PUZZLE 2

Sherlock Holmes and Dr. Watson had apprehended three men suspected of carrying out the Clapham bank robbery. The three men, Fish, Giles, and Hill, were taken to Scotland Yard, where they were interviewed by Inspector Lestrade. As Lestrade noted down the age of each of the men, he was aware that if he reversed each of the digits of their ages, all three men would still remain the same age. Lestrade also noticed that Fish was only a third the age of Giles, who in turn was twice the age of Hill. The combined age of all three men was 121 years.

How old was each of the three men?

Solution on page 87

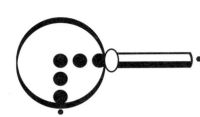

PUZZLE 3

While wearing one of his famous disguises, Sherlock Holmes followed a suspect through London's busy streets. The suspect entered two shops. In order not to look suspicious, Holmes purchased an item in each of the shops. In the first shop Holmes spent one-fourth of all his money, and in the second shop he spent one-fourth of what remained.

If Holmes spent £21 in total, how much did he have to begin with?

Solution on page 87

28

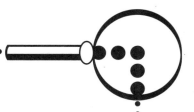

PUZZLE 4

Sherlock Holmes and Dr. Watson had been spectators at the annual Scotland Yard athletics meeting. Inspector Lestrade had done extremely well for his team. He was the first in two events and second in another. Lestrade's team had scored a total of 25 points, making them outright winners of the whole meeting. In each event points were awarded for first, second, and third place. Lestrade's team had gained their points by winning four events, coming in second in two and taking a third place in another.

How many points did Inspector Lestrade score for his team?

Solution on page 87

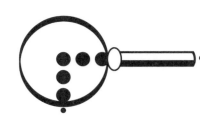

PUZZLE 5

Aston Avenue was a private row of only five houses numbered 1, 2, 3, 4, and 5. The owners of these houses were Messrs. Jones, White, Smith, Green, and Brown. All five houses had recently been robbed, and Sherlock Holmes called to speak with each of the owners. Unfortunately, all five were not at home. Holmes spoke with a passerby and was able to record the following facts:

1. Jones lived two doors to the left of Smith.
2. Brown and Green living on his right.
3. Both White and Brown lived in an even-numbered house.

From the above can you determine which house on Aston Avenue Mr. Green lived in?

Solution on page 87

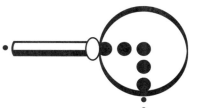

PUZZLE 6

Sherlock Holmes had received two telegrams from the infamous Professor Moriarty within a space of 3 hours. The first was a threat against the famous detective's life, while the second said that he, the professor, had organized a present for Holmes. The remainder of the second telegram contained the following riddle:

> He who makes it, makes it to sell,
> He who buys it, does not use it,
> He who uses it, does not know it.

Watson read both telegrams. "It doesn't make sense to me, Holmes," said Watson. "First he threatens your life and then he organizes a present for you."

"Solve the riddle, Watson. Then you'll see that it makes sense," replied Holmes.

What was it that Moriarty intended to send Holmes?

Solution on page 87

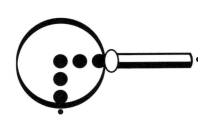

PUZZLE 7

Sherlock Holmes was questioning three men who had been witness to a murder, Messrs. Franks, Richards, and Andrews. By coincidence, their first names were Richard, Frank, and Andrew. Holmes remarked to Mr. Richards on this.

"Yes, I noticed that as well," he replied. "But none of us has the first name that matches our surname. My first name happens to be Andrew."

Can you give the full name of all three witnesses?

Solution on page 87

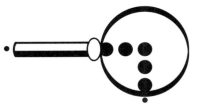

PUZZLE 8

Sherlock Holmes sat by the fire at 221b Baker Street, studying some information on a note.

"What's that you're reading, Holmes?" asked Watson as he entered.

"It's a list of houses on Fitzroy Street that have all been robbed in the last six days by Professor Moriarty."

Watson glanced at the list, which read:

Monday	No. 4
Tuesday	No. 16
Wednesday	No. 12
Thursday	No. 3
Friday	No. 7
Saturday	No. 28

"Great Scott!" exclaimed Watson. "And today's Sunday. He'll probably strike again tonight."

"He will, Watson," replied Holmes. "But this time we'll be waiting inside the house for him."

Which house on Fitzroy Street will Moriarty rob next?

*Solution on
page 87*

33

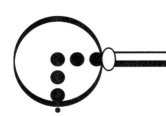

PUZZLE 9

Sherlock Holmes, Dr. Watson, and Inspector Lestrade were enjoying a cup of tea in the study of 221b Baker Street, when they were called away on an urgent matter. Each grabbed an overcoat and rushed from the house. It turned out that all three had grabbed the wrong overcoat.

"This coat is much too tight on me," remarked Lestrade to the person wearing Watson's coat.

Whose overcoat was each of them wearing?

Solution on page 87

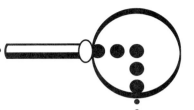

PUZZLE 10

Sherlock Holmes arrested the butler of the Westwood mansion for poisoning the entire Westwood family. After confessing, the butler went on to explain to Holmes just exactly how it was done. He filled a wineglass half full of wine, and another glass twice the size one-third full of wine. He then topped up each glass with poison before pouring the contents of both glasses into an empty wine decanter.

Can you deduce how much of the mixture is wine and how much is poison?

Solution on page 87

PUZZLE 11

To pass the time while traveling on a long train journey, Sherlock Holmes set his colleague, Dr. Watson, a little teaser to work out. See the diagram below:

7			=19
		5	=16
	3		=10

|| || || \\
15 16 14 17

"What do you want me to do with this, Holmes?" asked Watson.

"Simple, my dear Watson. Insert the following numbers in their proper place so that each column adds up to the number indicated. The missing numbers are: 4, 6, 1, 2, 8, 9."

By the time their train journey had ended, Watson had failed to complete the teaser correctly.

Can you do better?

Solution on page 87

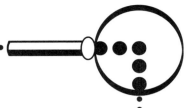

PUZZLE 12

Sherlock Holmes and Dr. Watson were running after a criminal in a crowded London street. They turned a corner only to find that the criminal was nowhere to be seen. Holmes turned to a beggar sitting at the side of the road. "Did you happen to see a man wearing a tall black hat and a cape pass this way?"

"Yes," replied the beggar.

"Which direction did he take?" asked Watson.

"Well, when I first saw him he was facing due east, but then he did a right turn, before taking a left turn and heading off in that direction."

Which way did the criminal go?

Solution on page 87

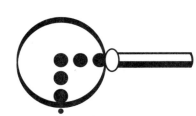

PUZZLE 13

A murderer had weighted down the body of his victim and dumped him in the Thames. Unknown to the murderer, the point where he dumped the body was much shallower than he had thought. Sherlock Holmes was called to the scene, where he discovered that the body was standing upright in the water. One-fourth of the victim was buried in the mud, five-eighths of the body was covered by water, and the remaining $9\frac{1}{2}$ inches protruded from the water.

Can you determine the height of the victim in feet and inches?

Solution on page 87

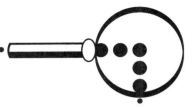

PUZZLE 14

Sherlock Holmes, Dr. Watson, and Inspector Lestrade were all involved in the solving of a recent murder. The day after the case was concluded, all three wrote individual reports on the crime. The combined number of pages written was 99. Lestrade wrote 5 more pages than Holmes, who in turn had submitted 17 more pages than Watson.

How many pages did each of them write?

Solution on page 87

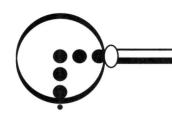

PUZZLE 15

Professor Moriarty had trapped Holmes and Watson in a room with no windows and only one door. After a few minutes, they could hear the sound of a pump starting up, and within moments the room began to fill with water. "Great Scott, we're going to drown!" shouted Watson.

Holmes moved over to the door, where he found it to be secured by a combination lock. There was a note pinned to the door in Moriarty's handwriting. The note revealed that the combination lock contained six numbers. The sum of the first two numbers was 69. The next two totalled 79, and the last two 29. At this point Holmes remembered something that Moriarty had said as he had closed them in the room. "It will help you, Holmes, if you remember that the difference between the first and second, the third and fourth, and the fifth and sixth is 13 in each case!" Holmes smiled as he set to work on the combination lock.

Can you find the six numbers that would open the door and release Holmes and Watson?

Solution on page 88

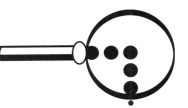

PUZZLE 16

Sherlock Holmes, Dr. Watson and Inspector Lestrade shared a cab to Euston Station, where they would each catch a train to separate destinations.

1. Holmes would not be taking the train to Brighton.
2. Watson wasn't taking the train to Manchester.
3. Lestrade wasn't taking the Edinburgh train.
4. The Brighton train left before Watson's train.

From the above information, can you discover the intended destinations of all three?

Solution on page 88

41

PUZZLE 17

Sherlock Holmes received an urgent telegram from a client. The client felt certain that his life was in danger. Holmes and Watson hurried to his lodgings only to find that they were too late. The man had been murdered minutes before they arrived.

"I found him lying there," said the landlady. "Before he died he muttered something about belonging to a secret club and quoted the number 92."

"Damned strange thing to say, Holmes," said Watson.

Holmes nodded in agreement. "Did he say anything else?" Holmes asked the landlady.

"I asked him who had done this terrible thing to him, but he just repeated the number 92!" she answered.

Holmes thanked her for her help and discharged her. He then proceeded to search the dead man's room. He came across a letter addressed to the man that was from the other three members of the secret club. Their names were Mr. Wilson, Mr. Updike, and Mr. Brown. In the top left of the letter was the name of the dead man, Mr. Smith (Code 69). From this, Holmes deduced that he had been murdered by another member of the club, and that the number that he had uttered to the landlady was in fact the code number of the murderer.

Holmes was then quickly able to supply the name of the killer. Can you?

Solution on page 88

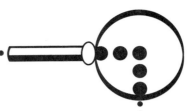

PUZZLE 18

Holmes glanced at a note that had been slipped under the door of 221b Baker Street.

"What is it, Holmes?" asked Watson, seeing the concern on the face of his colleague.

"It's a note from Moriarty. He intends to kidnap a prominent member of Parliament, and he has sent us a riddle as to the identity of the victim."

The riddle read: GREAT WISE OLD MAN, AT WILL.

Whom did Moriarty intend to kidnap?

Solution on page 88

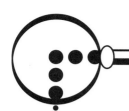

PUZZLE 19

Moriarty and his two partners in crime, Fingers and Porky, sat looking at the diamonds piled on the table in front of them. There was a knock at the door, which Porky answered. Mr. X, the brains behind the robbery, entered. Moriarty sent Porky to check the surrounding area to make sure that Mr. X had not been followed. Mr. X then took Porky's seat at the table. They sat in silence for several moments, until Moriarty bent forward and took half the diamonds plus one from the pile. Mr. X then took two-thirds of what remained, placed them in his pocket and, without a word, left the building. Fingers then took two-thirds of what remained and placed them in a bag. He smiled at Moriarty and took one more diamond, which he quickly shoved into the top pocket of his coat.

When Porky returned, he glanced down at the solitary diamond lying on the table. "Is this all I get, one measly diamond?" he grunted.

How many diamonds had originally been on the table?

Solution on page 88

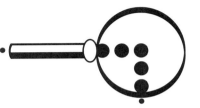

PUZZLE 20

Lord Knight invited Sherlock Holmes, Dr. Watson, and Inspector Lestrade to spend the weekend at his country estate. After showing the excellent stable facilities, Lord Knight suggested that they, along with the stables' head boy, Martin, should all take part in a horse race around the boundaries of the estate. Everybody readily agreed.

The last horse to finish was Fair Sensation. Ivory Tower finished first. Watson rode Kestrel. Lestrade's horse finished fourth. Holmes didn't finish second. Lord Knight finished three places behind Spring Goddess.

From the above information, can you identify:

1. Who rode Tinkerbell?
2. Which horse Martin rode?

Solution on page 88

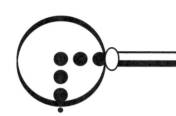

PUZZLE 21

Sherlock Holmes, Dr. Watson, and Mrs. Hudson left Baker Street to spend an evening at the theatre. In the foyer, they met Inspector Lestrade and Sergeant Baxter. All five had a drink in the theatre bar before taking their seats to enjoy the performance. All five sat in the same row together, taking up the seats numbererd 35, 36, 37, 38, and 39.

From the information below, can you identify the seats occupied by Inspector Lestrade and Sergeant Baxter?

1. Watson sat to the left of Holmes, but not directly.
2. Sergeant Baxter sat in an odd-numbered seat with Holmes directly on his right.
3. Mrs. Hudson sat to the left of Lestrade, but not directly.

Solution on page 88

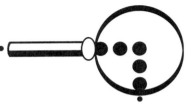

PUZZLE 22

Dr. Watson, who had been keeping an eye on events at Lady McBride's dinner party, reported back to Sherlock Holmes at 221b Baker Street.

"I need to know the arrival times of the guests, Watson," said Holmes.

Watson glanced at his notepad. "Yes, here it is. The arrival times are as follows," said Watson. "7:30, 7:45, 7:50, 7:59, 8:05, with the last guest arriving at 8:20."

"Very good, Watson," said Holmes. "But I need to know just exactly which guest arrived at which time."

"Oh," said Watson, somewhat embarrassed. "I didn't write that down, Holmes."

Eventually Watson was able to pass the following information to Holmes:

1. Lady Barclay, who wasn't the first to arrive, arrived before Lord Hadden.
2. Sir Harry Trump arrived 15 minutes after Lord Winterbottom.
3. It was one of the ladies who arrived 6 minutes after Sir John Penn.
4. Lady James arrived 15 minutes before Lord Hadden.

Can you deduce the exact arrival time of each of the six guests?

Solution on page 88

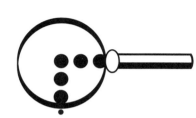

PUZZLE 23

Sherlock Holmes was traveling by train from London to Brighton. Five other gentlemen shared the compartment with him. They were Messrs. Andrews, Baker, Clark, Dawson, and Easton. It turned out that each of these gentlemen lived on a London street that bore the name of one of the others.

From the following information, can you match up each of the five men with the street where he lived?

1. Mr. Andrews sat between Sherlock Holmes and the other gentleman who lived on Baker Street.
2. Mr. Baker, who sat opposite Mr. Dawson, had the gentleman who lived on Clark Street sitting next to him.
3. The gentleman opposite Holmes lived on Easton Street.

Solution on page 88

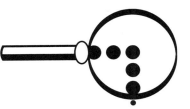

PUZZLE 24

Miss Aldridge, who ran a large boarding house in Acton town, had sent a telegram to Sherlock Holmes requesting his help on a matter of great importance. Within an hour of receiving the telegram, Holmes and his assistant, Dr. Watson, arrived at the large house on Acton High Street.

"I'm quite concerned," said Miss Aldridge as she led them into the parlor. "I'm positive that one of my guests is trying to poison me."

"How many guests do you have?" asked Watson as he sat down in front of the roaring fire.

"Quite a few," replied the old lady. "Half of them are salesmen, a quarter of them teach at the local college, and one-seventh are shop owners. There are also three widowed ladies, but I don't suspect any of them."

From the above information, can you figure out how many guests lived at the boarding house?

Solution on page 88

PUZZLE 25

"I'm puzzled," said Lady Ashton to Sherlock Holmes. "One of my four servants has stolen my gold bracelet. I've questioned each of them, but I'm still none the wiser. Branson, the butler, said that Smythe, the gardener, did it, while Mary, the maid, said Smythe told her that Branson did it. Smythe told me Branson did it, and Wilson, the handyman, said he knew which one was the thief but he did not wish to say." Lady Ashton sighed, then continued, "I've known Branson and Smythe for many years and I've never known either of them to tell the truth."

Sherlock Holmes smiled as he filled his pipe. "Assuming that the butler and the gardener have not changed their ways, and that Mary and Wilson are telling the truth, it is quite a simple task to deduce which of them is the thief," said Holmes.

Can you work out which one of the staff stole the bracelet?

Solution on page 88

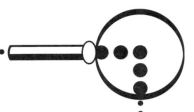

PUZZLE 26

Sherlock Holmes and Dr. Watson were enjoying a quiet drink in the members' lounge of the Criminologist's Club when four men entered by way of the private office. "Ah, here come the four new committee members," announced Holmes.

"I don't recognize any of them," said Watson.

"Before you stand the chairman, vice-chairman, treasurer, and secretary," replied Holmes. "Their surnames are Hopkins, Smythe, White, and Knight."

Holmes then went on to explain that the treasurer and the chairman were cousins, that Hopkins and Smythe were not related to each other, that the vice-chairman's wife was a well-known actress, and that the secretary was engaged to Lord Winterbottom's daughter.

He also pointed out that White and the treasurer were not on speaking terms, and that Hopkins and White were the only ones who were married.

Can you identify each committee member's new position within the club?

Solution on page 88

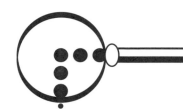

PUZZLE 27

"I'm bored," said Dr. Watson to Sherlock Holmes. "This train journey seems to be going on forever."

Sherlock Holmes smiled at his companion and took a sheet of paper from his coat pocket. On the sheet of paper Holmes drew a large square. He then divided this square into sixteen squares (see diagram). He then took four coins from his pocket and asked Watson to place each coin on one of the squares in such a way that no two coins ended up in the same row either horizontally, vertically or diagonally.

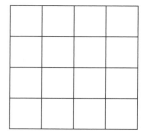

Can you achieve this? (There are several possible solutions.)

Solution on page 88

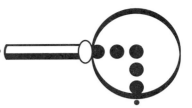

PUZZLE 28

"It was undoubtedly one of the staff who murdered Lord Backwater," said Sherlock Holmes to Dr. Watson. "Have you interviewed them?"

"Yes," replied Watson, glancing at his notes. "It turns out that the maid is the sister of the butler's granddaughter, who in turn, is the gardener's brother's mother."

From the above information, can you tell how the gardener and the butler were related?

Solution on page 88

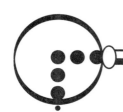

PUZZLE 29

After some clever groundwork by Sherlock Holmes, Inspector Lestrade was able to arrest three criminals. Between them they were charged with thirty-seven different offenses.

If Harold was charged with five more offenses than John, and Robert was charged with six more offenses than Harold, how many offenses had each of them committed?

Solution on page 88

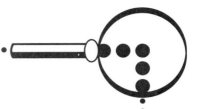

PUZZLE 30

On a cold winter's evening Sherlock Holmes and Dr. Watson sat in the comfort of a blazing fire at their residence at 221b Baker Street. After a long bout of silence Sherlock Holmes spoke. "Take the word 'sparkling,' Watson. Take away one letter so as to leave a new word. Then continue this procedure, leaving a new word on each occasion until you are left with a one-letter word."

Watson sat for some time before finally coming up with an answer.

Can you?

Solution on page 88

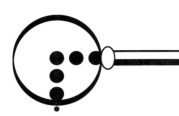

PUZZLE 31

When Lady Sharp reported the kidnapping of her young son to Sherlock Holmes, Holmes knew that the crime could only have been carried out by one man—Professor Moriarty.

Lady Sharp produced a ransom note for £10,000. The note also carried a warning that should the money not be paid, she would never see her son alive again. As Lady Sharp left 221b Baker Street, a note was delivered by hand to Sherlock Holmes. "Blast!" cried Holmes as he read the note before passing it to Dr. Watson. "Moriarty knows that we are on the case, Watson. We must act quickly if we are to save the life of Lady Sharp's son!"

Watson read the note. "I don't understand, Holmes. This note is nothing more than gobbledegook!"

"Not so, Watson," cried Holmes as he grabbed his coat. "Unless we find Moriarty's hiding place quickly, we will be too late to find Lady Sharp's son alive!"

The note read: HATED HALLS TEAK STREAM HARPS TOADY!

Can you decipher the note?

Solution on page 88

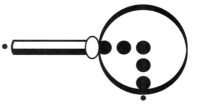

PUZZLE 32

Sherlock Holmes sat opposite Inspector Lestrade in Lestrade's office at Scotland Yard. Sergeant Smith entered with three prisoners, who were stood in a line in front of Lestrade's desk. Holmes watched with interest as Lestrade interrogated the three men.

Barnett stood between the man who was clean-shaven and the man who had stolen a cigar case. Black, who had stolen the wallet, had been arrested at the same time as Wetherby. It was the man with the mustache, not the one with the beard, who had stolen the gold watch.

Can you identify each of the men, matching them to:

1. The item each had stolen, and
2. Whether each was clean-shaven or had a mustache or a beard?

Solution on page 89

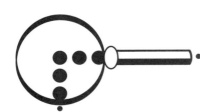

PUZZLE 33

During the course of one night Professor Moriarty robbed five jewellers, taking only diamonds from each one. During his investigation, Sherlock Holmes discovered that one jeweller had lost $\frac{1}{4}$ of the total diamonds stolen, another had lost $\frac{1}{3}$, a third had lost $\frac{1}{6}$, the fourth had lost $\frac{1}{12}$, and the last jeweller had lost a total of 22 diamonds.

How many diamonds had been stolen altogether?

Solution on page 89

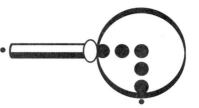

PUZZLE 34

Sherlock Holmes and Dr. Watson were following three criminals who had carried out a bank robbery to Euston railway station. Unfortunately, all three had managed to escape before Holmes and Watson arrived at the station. Holmes interviewed several railway employees and discovered that all three had boarded trains to different destinations. Parker, the leader of the trio, did not take the train to Carlisle. Davidson didn't take the Liverpool train and Costello didn't take the Glasgow train. He also discovered that the Carlisle train left the station before the train taken by Davidson. Holmes knew that each of the three had taken a train to one of the above-mentioned destinations.

Can you find out the destination of each of the criminals?

Solution on page 89

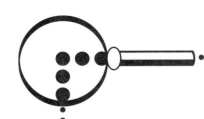

PUZZLE 35

As five petty criminals left a tavern one evening, they were promptly arrested by Inspector Lestrade. After escorting them back to Scotland Yard, he made them take out the contents of their pockets. Between them they had some £70 in cash.

From the following information, can you determine just exactly how much each of them had?

1. Brown had £3 more than Adams.
2. Clark had £3 more than Brown.
3. Drake had £6 more than Brown
4. Evans had £12 more than Adams.

Solution on page 89

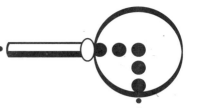

PUZZLE 36

While working on a series of robberies, Sherlock Holmes and Dr. Watson interviewed ten people, each of whom had a different occupation. Listed below are the ten occupations in anagram form.

Can you unravel each of them and identify the ten occupations?

1. STRIPE
2. LEWDER
3. LAMINAR
4. REWARD
5. CRANED

6. HECTARE
7. STINTED
8. BREAK
9. RESIGN
10. CORKED

Solution on page 89

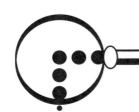

PUZZLE 37

Sherlock Holmes and Dr. Watson had followed two counterfeiters to their secret printing place. They waited outside for quite some time before bursting in and taking the two men by surprise. Next to the printing press they found some £5,000 in forged bills. Holmes then asked the two men to empty out their pockets. Thereupon Holmes recovered £227 more in forged bills.

If one forger had £55 more than the other, how much did each of them have in his pocket?

Solution on page 89

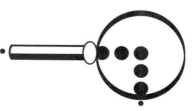

PUZZLE 38

Sherlock Holmes and Dr. Watson were called to the Royal Mint, where they were informed by an executive that there was at least one thief in the building. Over a period of several days, a large number of gold coins had disappeared. Holmes decided to set a trap. He placed a box containing a number of gold coins in an area where it was easily accessible to everybody in the building. He and Watson then hid themselves behind some large cabinets to observe the scene. After a few minutes, a man appeared, looked inside the box, and removed a third of the coins. Only seconds later, the man returned and removed a third of what remained. Some 10 minutes later, another man appeared and he proceeded to remove a third of what remained. Holmes then checked the box to find that only eight gold coins remained.

How many gold coins had originally been in the box?

Solution on page 89

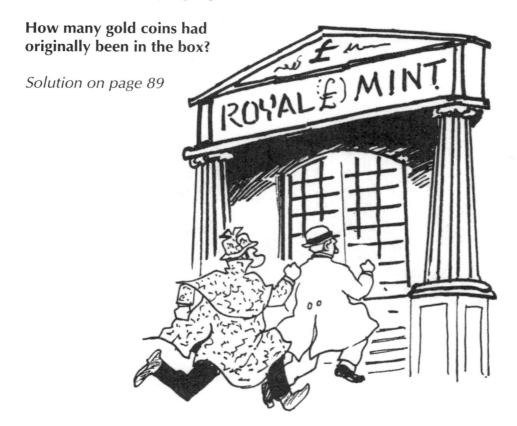

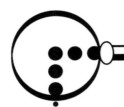

PUZZLE 39

Professor Moriarty was about to carry out a daring robbery with two other criminals, Stoneface Murphy and Fingers Malloy. In order that none of them would be recognized, they each wore a false beard. They were also armed. One carried a rifle, another a pistol, and the third a club. Moriarty entered the bank behind the one who wore the false brown beard and in front of the one who carried the club. Fingers had used the pistol in a previous robbery and was disappointed that he didn't have it on this occasion. It was the one with the false red beard who carried the club.

If Fingers did not wear the false brown beard, who carried the club?

Solution on page 89

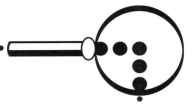

PUZZLE 40

Sherlock Holmes had been hired to find three boys who had run away from home. His inquiries had taken him to the London docks and, in particular, the ocean liner *Celestial Star*. After carrying out a search of the ship, he discovered the three boys hiding inside one of the ship's lifeboats.

"How old are they?" exclaimed the captain as the boys stepped onto the deck.

"Their combined age is 27 years," replied Holmes. "Tommy is twice as old as Eric, while James is three-quarters the age of Tommy."

Can you deduce the age of each of the three boys?

Solution on page 89

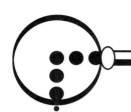

PUZZLE 41

Sherlock Holmes and Dr. Watson were in the small kitchen of Fredrick Blake, the retired gardener at Greenacres Mansion. Fredrick lay dead on the floor, the victim of a ghastly murder.

Dr. Watson pointed to a stain on the wooden floorboards where Fredrick lay. "This looks like some sort of acid burn, Holmes," he said.

"Very observant of you, Watson," replied Holmes. "Take a look at these items on the kitchen table. There are acids contained in each one of them. Can you name them, Watson?"

The items on the table were:
1. Vinegar
2. Green apples
3. Tea

Can you name the types of acid in each case?

Solution on page 89

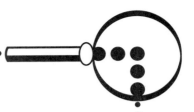

PUZZLE 42

In a warehouse, Sherlock Holmes came across some crates set out in a triangle (see diagram). All the crates (apart from the one at the head of the triangle) were numbered.

Can you deduce the number of the last crate?

Solution on page 89

8	5	4	3

13	9	7

22	16

?

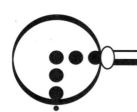

PUZZLE 43

During a cricket match, Sherlock Holmes scored 90 more runs than Inspector Lestrade. He, in turn, scored 70 fewer runs than Inspector Brown. Dr. Watson scored 20 more runs than Sergeant Smith. Inspector Brown scored 40 more runs than Dr. Watson.

If Inspector Lestrade and Dr. Watson scored 50 runs between them, how many runs did all the above players score altogether?

Solution on page 89

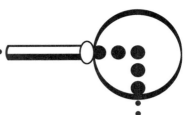

PUZZLE 42

In a warehouse, Sherlock Holmes came across some crates set out in a triangle (see diagram). All the crates (apart from the one at the head of the triangle) were numbered.

Can you deduce the number of the last crate?

Solution on page 89

8	5	4	3
	13	9	7
		22	16
			?

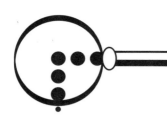

PUZZLE 43

During a cricket match, Sherlock Holmes scored 90 more runs than Inspector Lestrade. He, in turn, scored 70 fewer runs than Inspector Brown. Dr. Watson scored 20 more runs than Sergeant Smith. Inspector Brown scored 40 more runs than Dr. Watson.

If Inspector Lestrade and Dr. Watson scored 50 runs between them, how many runs did all the above players score altogether?

Solution on page 89

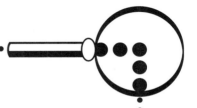

PUZZLE 44

Sherlock Holmes and Dr. Watson were about to interview three men regarding a recent robbery at Fanshaw Manor. The three men were sitting outside Inspector Lestrade's office in Scotland Yard.

"Who are they?" asked Watson.

"A Mr. Black, Mr. Grey, and Mr. Brown," replied Holmes.

"How amazing," said Watson, "They're wearing suits that match their names."

"Perfectly correct, Watson," said Holmes, "But not one of them is wearing the precise color of suit that matches his own name."

"Then Mr. Black is wearing the brown suit," said Watson with some confidence.

"Not so," replied Holmes.

Can you deduce the color suit each of the three men was wearing?

Solution on page 89

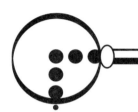

PUZZLE 45

Sherlock Holmes studied the dead victim who lay on the library floor. Dr. Watson entered the room. "I've spoken with the maid and she is quite adamant that she heard the shot ring out at 12:15 PM, Holmes," he announced, "which completely destroys your theory that the deed took place some time earlier."

"I still feel she is mistaken, Watson," said Holmes with some confidence.

"I doubt it, Holmes," replied Watson. "She was dusting in the study when she heard the shot. She remembers standing bolt upright at the sound of the blast and she remembers looking directly into the mirror and seeing the clock behind her. It was unmistakably 12:15 PM."

Holmes smiled at his colleague, "Then I was correct all along, Watson," he exclaimed.

What time did the maid actually hear the shot?

Solution on page 89

70

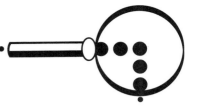

PUZZLE 46

While sitting in his study, Sherlock Holmes was handed a piece of paper by his colleague, Dr. Watson. On the paper was written the following sequence of numbers:

45	32	31	42
34			37
38			41
33	44	43	30

"What is this, Watson?" asked Holmes.

"This is my magic square," Watson replied. "The numbers add up to the same total in each direction. But I have deliberately left out the four center numbers. Can you tell me what they are?"

Watson was disappointed that Holmes was able to supply the numbers within a matter of seconds.

Can you do it?

Solution on page 89

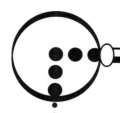

PUZZLE 47

Professor Moriarty had set up a system of robbing all the houses on an exclusive London street. The street contained 25 houses and they were numbered accordingly.

On the diagram below, can you fill in the question marks with the correct number of houses to complete the system?

?	24	1	8	15
23	?	7	14	16
4	6	?	20	22
10	12	19	?	3
11	18	25	2	?

Solution on page 89

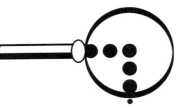

PUZZLE 48

Sherlock Holmes, Dr. Watson, Inspector Lestrade, and Sergeant Smith were all playing for the Scotland Yard select cricket team in a charity match. While in the locker room getting ready for the match, each of the four accidentally put on a jersey belonging to one of the others.

From the following information, can you figure out whose jersey each of them was wearing?

1. Watson wasn't wearing the jersey that belonged to Lestrade.
2. Holmes didn't wear Watson's jersey nor vice versa.
3. Sergeant Smith went to bat ahead of the person wearing Watson's jersey.

Solution on page 90

73

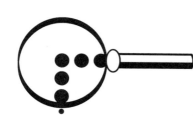

PUZZLE 49

Sherlock Holmes and Dr. Watson were walking along a quiet street when they both observed the following sequence of letters written on a wall:

I C A B
I C A U
I C A X
I C A P

Below the sequence of letters was written: "One of these rows of letters does not belong to the series. Which one?"

Holmes was quick to supply the answer. Can you?

Solution on page 90

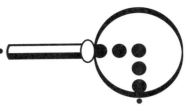

PUZZLE 50

While working on a murder case, Sherlock Holmes, Dr. Watson, and Inspector Lestrade found themselves searching a desolate Yorkshire moor for the murder weapon. During the search, they were assisted by a police sergeant and a constable. Before the weapon was found, every one of them had covered a lot of ground in their search.

From the following information, can you deduce just exactly how much ground was covered by Inspector Lestrade?

1. Holmes, Watson, and the constable had covered 9 miles between them.
2. Lestrade, Watson, and the sergeant covered 16 miles.
3. Watson, Holmes, and Lestrade covered 12 miles, while the total number of miles covered by Lestrade and the constable was 7.

Solution on page 90

PUZZLE 51

Sherlock Holmes, Dr. Watson, Mrs. Hudson, Inspector Lestrade, and Sergeant Black all decided to spend a night in a supposedly haunted mansion. Just before midnight, they all traveled (in separate hansom cabs) to the country mansion.

From the following information, can you figure out which one of them arrived fourth at the mansion?

1. Watson's cab arrived before that of Black, but behind the cab carrying Holmes.
2. Mrs. Hudson's cab arrived before Watson's, but behind the cab carrying Holmes.

Solution on page 90

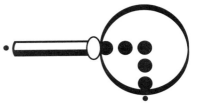

PUZZLE 52

Sherlock Holmes and Dr. Watson were called to a jewelry shop on Oxford Street where a number of precious stones had been stolen in a daring robbery.

From the following information, can you deduce just how many diamonds were stolen?

1. A combined total of 29 diamonds, rubies, and garnets was stolen.
2. A combined total of 31 rubies, garnets, and sapphires was stolen.
3. A combined total of 18 diamonds and sapphires was stolen.

Solution on page 90

PUZZLE 53

Dr. Watson was sitting in the study of 221b Baker Street examining the night sky with his telescope when Sherlock Holmes entered the room and passed him a piece of paper.

"Written on the paper, Watson, is a series of letters," said Holmes. "Since you are observing the stars, you should have little difficulty finding the three missing letters from the series."

On the paper was written the following sequence of letters:

S U I R A ? ? ?

Can you complete the series?

Solution on page 90

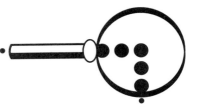

PUZZLE 54

Professor Moriarty and three of his criminal colleagues rushed from a hardware shop, each carrying a handful of money which he had stolen from the poor owner. In total they had £94. Moriarty had £13 more than Bloggs, who in turn had £5 less than Norris, while Hunt had £3 more than Moriarty.

Can you deduce how much each of the four carried individually?

Solution on page 90

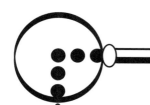

PUZZLE 55

Sherlock Holmes had been called to a small London hotel to investigate a series of robberies from rooms occupied by guests.

Can you place each guest in the exact room he occupied in the hotel from the following information (see diagram below)?

(12 bedrooms)

3rd floor			
2nd floor			
1st floor			

1. Messrs. Smith, Idle, and Law were all on the floor above the floor where Messrs. Jones and Grey had their rooms.
2. Mr. Black's room was directly above the room occupied by Mr. Davis and directly to the right of the room occupied by Mr. Grey.
3. Messrs. Green, Adams, and White were all on the floor below the floor where Mr. Wilson had his room.
4. Mr. Brown's room was directly above that of Mr. Jones, who in turn was directly to the right of Mr. Wilson.
5. Mr. Idle had Mr. Law directly to his right.
6. Mr. White was directly below Mr. Grey and directly to the right of Mr. Adams.

Solution on page 90

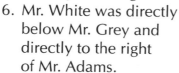

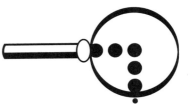

PUZZLE 56

While spending a weekend fishing in the country, Sherlock Holmes and Dr. Watson were asked to investigate a series of robberies that had taken place at three cottages which were situated close to the fishing lodge where they were staying.

From the following information, can you name the family that lived at each cottage and the item they had had stolen by the robbers?

1. The Madisons didn't live at No. 3, nor did they lose a gold watch.
2. The O'Connors didn't live at No. 5.
3. £50 was stolen from No. 3.
4. The Newtons didn't live at No.1, where a crystal decanter was stolen.

Solution on page 90

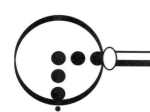

PUZZLE 57

Five pickpockets were arrested by Inspector Lestrade on evidence supplied by Sherlock Holmes. They were escorted back to Scotland Yard, where they were found to have some £95 in cash between them.

From the following information, can you determine just exactly how much each of them had?

1. Smith had £3 more than Jones.
2. Montgomery had £4 more than Smith.
3. Marr had £5 more than Jones.
4. Morgan had £12 less than Montgomery.

Solution on page 90

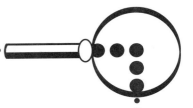

PUZZLE 58

While serving a prison sentence in Wormwood Scrubs Prison, Professor Moriarty made five separate escape attempts on each day from Monday to Friday. On each attempt, he tried a different method: a) Disguised as a prison officer. b) Tried to tunnel from his cell. c) Attempted to bribe a prison officer. d) Exchanged identity with a visitor. e) Attempted to sneak out with a work party.

From the following information, can you determine which method was used on which day?

1. Moriarty attempted to escape disguised as a prison officer two days before his attempted bribe of a prison officer.
2. He tried to tunnel out of his cell the day after his attempt disguised as a prison officer.
3. His attempt to sneak out with the work party didn't take place on Monday or Friday.
4. Moriarty exchanged identity with a visitor the day after his attempt to join the work party.

Solution on page 90

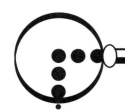

PUZZLE 59

Dr. Watson purchased six garden ornaments, which he duly placed around the back garden at 221b Baker Street, only to find that when he awoke the next morning, some thief had made off with them all. "They cost me a fortune," he complained to Sherlock Holmes. The six items had individually cost Watson £4, £10, £12, £15, £18, and £24.

From the following information, can you work out the exact items for each of the above prices?

1. The statue of Peter Pan cost £3 less than the statue of Admiral Nelson.
2. The fishing gnome cost £8 more than the hanging basket.
3. The reading gnome cost £14 less than the small fountain.

Solution on page 90

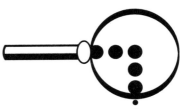

PUZZLE 60

As a result of excellent work by Sherlock Holmes, the infamous Professor Moriarty was being held in the special security wing of Wormwood Scrubs Prison. In all, there were twelve cells in the special wing, four on each landing (see diagram below).

From the following information, can you place each prisoner in his proper cell?

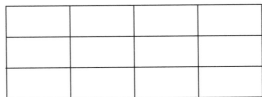

1. Little's cell was on the landing directly below the landing where Robb and Gunn had their cells.
2. Pearce's cell was directly above Conn's cell, who was on the landing above the landing where Hobbs and Webb had their cells.
3. Field had his cell directly to the right of Webb's cell and was directly below the cell occupied by Robb.
4. Tibbs had his cell directly to the left of Milne's cell, which was directly above Moriarty's.
5. Kidd's cell was directly to the left of the cell occupied by Pearce.
6. Moriarty was in the cell directly above the cell occupied by Webb.
7. Hobbs' cell was directly below Gunn's cell.

Solution on page 90

PUZZLE 61

The infamous Professor Moriarty had masterminded a massive bank robbery which meant a loss of many thousands of pounds for the bank concerned. By the time Sherlock Holmes was called in to investigate the robbery, it had been discovered that five leather pouches containing valuable Spanish gold coins had also been stolen. The gold coins totalled 111 in all.

From the following information, can you figure out how many gold coins were contained in each of the five pouches?

1. The combined number of coins in pouches 1 and 2 was 40.
2. The combined number of coins in pouches 2 and 3 was 35.
3. The combined number of coins in pouches 3 and 4 was 42.
3. The combined number of coins in pouches 4 and 5 was 54.

Solution on page 90

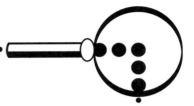

SOLUTIONS

PUZZLE 1 (page 26)
The numbers represent the vowels, 2 = A, 3 = E, etc. Then by breaking the message up into words, it reads: Tomorrow I will steal the crown jewels. This will be my greatest triumph.

PUZZLE 2 (page 27)
Fish 22 years. Hill 33 years. Giles 66 years.

PUZZLE 3 (page 28)
£48.

PUZZLE 4 (page 29)
12 points. 5 points were awarded for first place, 2 points for second, and 1 point for third.

PUZZLE 5 (page 30)
Number 5 Aston Avenue.

PUZZLE 6 (page 31)
A coffin.

PUZZLE 7 (page 32)
Andrew Richards, Frank Andrews, Richard Franks.

PUZZLE 8 (page 33)
No. 24. The pattern: $4 \times 4 = 16 - 4 = 12 \div 4 = 3 + 4 = 7 \times 4 = 28 - 4 = 24$

PUZZLE 9 (page 34)
Lestrade was wearing the over-coat belonging to Holmes, while Holmes wore Watson's and Watson wore Lestrade's.

PUZZLE 10 (page 35)
The wine in the smaller glass was one-sixth of the total liquid, while the wine in the larger glass was two-ninths of the total. Add these together to reveal that the wine was seven-eighteenths. Therefore the poison content has to be eleven-eighteenths.

PUZZLE 11 (page 36)

7	4	8	=19
2	9	5	=16
6	3	1	=10
15	16	14	17

PUZZLE 12 (page 37)
West.

PUZZLE 13 (page 38)
6 feet, 4 inches.

PUZZLE 14 (page 39)
Lestrade wrote 42 pages, Holmes wrote 37 pages, and Watson 20 pages.

PUZZLE 15 (page 40)
41 and 28 (69), 46 and 33 (79), 21 and 8 (29).

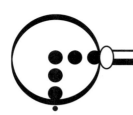

PUZZLE 16 (page 41)
Holmes was travelling to Manchester, Watson to Edinburgh, and Lestrade to Brighton.

PUZZLE 17 (page 42)
Wilson. The code numbers were devised by taking each letter of the member's surname and relating each one to its place in the alphabet. A = 1, B = 2, etc. Wilson consists of the 23rd, 9th, 12th, 19th, 15th, and 14th. Added together they make 92.

PUZZLE 18 (page 43)
William Ewart Gladstone (the Prime Minister).

PUZZLE 19 (page 44)
38 diamonds.

PUZZLE 20 (page 45)
Lestrade rode Tinkerbell, while Martin rode Spring Goddess.

PUZZLE 21 (page 46)
Inspector Lestrade occupied seat number 39, while Sergeant Baxter had seat number 37.

PUZZLE 22 (page 47)
The guests arrived as follows: 7:30 Lord Winterbottom. 7:45 Sir Harry Trump. 7:50 Lady Barclay. 7:59 Sir John Penn. 8:05 Lady James. 8:20 Lord Hadden.

PUZZLE 23 (page 48)
Mr. Baker/Andrews Street.
Mr. Andrews/Dawson Street.
Mr. Clark/Easton Street.
Mr. Dawson/Baker Street.
Mr. Easton/Clark Street.

PUZZLE 24 (page 49)
28 guests.

PUZZLE 25 (page 50)
Mary.

PUZZLE 26 (page 51)
Hopkins is the vice-chairman. White is the chairman. Smythe is the secretary. Knight is the treasurer.

PUZZLE 27 (page 52)
Here is one possibility.

PUZZLE 28 (page 53)
The gardener is the butler's great-grandson.

PUZZLE 29 (page 54)
John committed 7 offenses, Harold 12 offenses, and Robert 18.

PUZZLE 30 (page 55)
Sparkling, Sparking, Sparing, Spring, Sprig, Prig, Pig, Pi, and finally "I."

PUZZLE 31 (page 56)
Death shall take Master Sharp today.

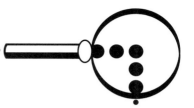

PUZZLE 32 (page 57)
Barnett: Mustache. Gold watch.
Wetherby: Beard. Cigar case.
Black: Clean-shaven. Wallet.

PUZZLE 33 (page 58)
132 diamonds.

PUZZLE 34 (page 59)
Parker was aboard the Liverpool train, Davidson aboard the Glasgow train, and Costello aboard the train bound for Carlisle.

PUZZLE 35 (page 60)
Adams had £8. Brown had £11. Clark had £14. Drake had £17. Evans had £20.

PUZZLE 36 (page 61)
1. Priest. 2. Welder. 3. Railman. 4. Warder. 5. Dancer. 6. Teacher. 7. Dentist. 8. Baker. 9. Singer. 10. Docker.

PUZZLE 37 (page 62)
One forger had £141 and the other had £86.

PUZZLE 38 (page 63)
27 coins

PUZZLE 39 (page 64)
Fingers carried the club.

PUZZLE 40 (page 65)
Tommy 12 years, James 9 years, and Eric 6 years.

PUZZLE 41 (page 66)
1. Acetic acid. 2. Malic acid. 3. Tannic acid.

PUZZLE 42 (page 67)
The number of the last crate is 38. The number on each crate is found by adding together the number of the two crates directly above it.

PUZZLE 43 (page 68)
250 runs. Sherlock Holmes 100 runs. Inspector Lestrade 10 runs. Inspector Brown 80 runs. Sergeant Smith 20 runs. Dr. Watson 40 runs.

PUZZLE 44 (page 69)
Mr. Brown (black suit), Mr. Black (grey suit), Mr. Grey (brown suit).

PUZZLE 45 (page 70)
11:45 AM.

PUZZLE 46 (page 71)

45	32	31	42
34	39	40	37
38	35	36	41
33	44	43	30

PUZZLE 47 (page 72)
Each column adds up to 65.

17	24	1	8	15
23	5	7	14	16
4	6	13	20	22
10	12	19	21	3
11	18	25	2	9

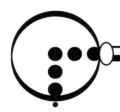

PUZZLE 48 (page 73)
Holmes was wearing Lestrade's jersey, Watson was wearing Smith's, Lestrade wore Watson's, and Smith wore Holmes's.

PUZZLE 49 (page 74)
I C A X. The other letters when read aloud all mean something: I see a bee, I see a ewe, I see a pea.

PUZZLE 50 (page 75)
5 miles.

PUZZLE 51 (page 76)
Watson.

PUZZLE 52 (page 77)
8 diamonds.

PUZZLE 53 (page 78)
U, Q, and A. The complete series reads: S U I R A U Q A. Aquarius spelled backwards.

PUZZLE 54 (page 79)
Moriarty had £28, Bloggs £15, Norris £20, Hunt £31.

PUZZLE 55 (page 80)

Smith	Brown	Idle	Law
Wilson	Jones	Grey	Black
Green	Adams	White	Davis

PUZZLE 56 (page 81)
The Madisons lived at No. 1 and lost the decanter. The Newtons lived at No. 5 and lost the gold watch. The O'Connors lived at No. 3 and lost the £50.

PUZZLE 57 (page 82)
Montgomery had £24. Marr had £22. Smith had £20. Jones had £17. Morgan had £12.

PUZZLE 58 (page 83)
Monday: Disguised as a prison officer. Tuesday: Tried to tunnel from his cell. Wednesday: Tried to bribe a prison officer. Thursday: Tried to join the work party. Friday: Exchanged identity with a visitor.

PUZZLE 59 (page 84)
Hanging basket £4, reading gnome £10, fishing gnome £12, Peter Pan £15, Admiral Nelson £18, small fountain £24.

PUZZLE 60 (page 85)

Tibbs	Milne	Kidd	Pearce
Gunn	Moriarty	Robb	Conn
Hobbs	Webb	Field	Little

PUZZLE 61 (page 86)
Pouch 1 = 22 coins. Pouch 2 = 18. Pouch 3 = 17. Pouch 4 = 25. Pouch 5 = 29.

INSPECTOR FORSOOTH'S
WHODUNITS

DERRICK NIEDERMAN

ILLUSTRATED BY
MATT LaFLEUR

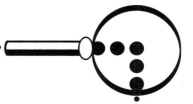

INTRODUCTION

THE MYSTERIES IN THIS BOOK are like no others you've ever tried. For starters, they've all been tested live—in an America Online "auditorium"—in front of hundreds of cybersleuths. These intrepid sleuths would read the mystery text and then fire literally thousands of questions at yours truly, Inspector Forsooth. The questions and answers that accompany each mystery are taken directly from these online solving sessions.

Sound interesting? Good. It gets even better.

These mysteries go far beyond the "one-shot wonder" format that dominates the mini-mystery genre. (You've seen such stories, I'm sure. Like the English professor who "committed suicide" and left a note filled with grammatical errors.) Such mysteries can be entertaining— I've tried hundreds of them myself. But aren't you ready for something a bit more challenging? Something new and different? You've come to the right place.

Each of the mysteries in this book contains a mosaic of clues that the sleuth (that's you) must piece together to divine the solution. You will be aided by the question-and-answer session—an edited version of the real-time, online chaos—which flushes out each and every tiny clue hidden in the text. You can read all the answers or test yourself by reading only a few. It's all up to you.

I feel I should warn you, though: These mysteries are hard! They're not child's play. But I'm confident you'll love the challenges I have for you.

Inspector Forsooth
Cybersleuth Extraordinaire

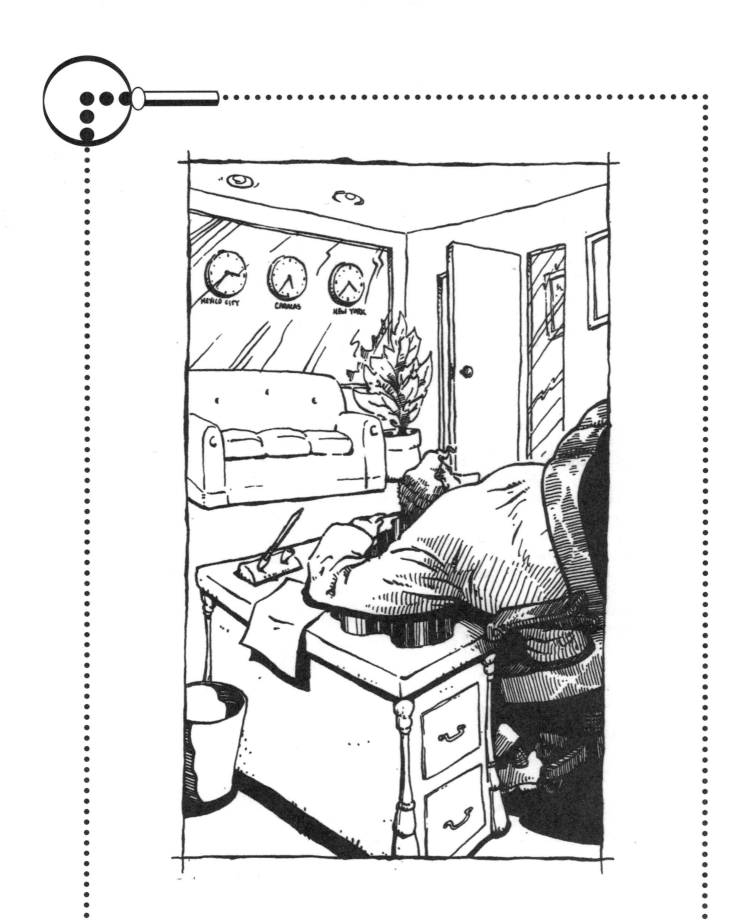

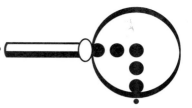

MURDER AROUND THE CLOCK

BRUCE BERRINGER WAS A SUCCESSFUL MAN, but he paid a high price. When all was said and done, his success cost him his life.

Berringer was born and raised in the small town of Bogusville, near the Colorado/Utah border. His was a blue-collar community, and the townsfolk were the sort of friendly, hardworking, generous souls that so often come out of rural America. But Berringer wanted more. He wanted money, prestige, and a name for himself in international business circles.

He had the smarts, the drive, and the connections to make good on his dream. His father was a Navy man who had traveled all over the world prior to returning to Bogusville, and Bruce's business savvy parlayed these far-flung contacts into a thriving importing enterprise: pottery, belts, wicker—you name it. Berringer Imports grew to the point where it had satellite offices literally around the world. But rather than leave his roots, Berringer delighted in keeping his main office right at home, knowing he could parade his success in front of all those who thought he'd never amount to anything in this world.

As a result of Berringer's obsession with fame, friendships suffered. His childhood cronies noticed that Berringer judged them by what they did for a living and not who they were as people. None of them made one-tenth the money Berringer did, and his scorn was always there.

One night there was a big party at Berringer Imports to celebrate the landing of a new international account. Five of Bruce's friends from high school showed up. They didn't necessarily want to be there, and they certainly didn't fit in with the corporate types who flew in for the occasion; but in some sense it was worse to be left out of the lavish Berringer celebrations than to suffer through one night. Liked or not, Berringer was the most powerful figure in town, and he could be very vengeful when people didn't play the games he wanted them to.

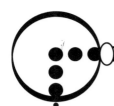

The cronies included Rafael Betz, who owned a catering business and was doing well in his own right, in no small part because he had the opportunity to cater many of Berringer's parties, including this particular one. Then there was Frank Dowling, a plumbing contractor, who complained that the ultra-rich Berringer was incredibly cheap, haggling over charges that normal people would pay without comment. The other local guests were rated even lower on Berringer's importance scale. There was Sean McGillicuddy, whose DairyFresh route took him to the outskirts of the Berringer estate but never any farther, and there was Jimmie Wu, who scratched out a living by refereeing local high school athletic contests, including many involving Berringer's spoiled son Yancey. About the only one of Berringer's buddies who looked comfortable at this black-tie affair was Benjamin Walters, but only because he was accustomed to formalities. Walters was the maître d' at the swank Olivia's restaurant, which was starting with money from —you guessed it—Bruce Berringer. Berringer even got a rare laugh by raising his arm and calling out "Maître d'!" upon spying Walters at the party in his usual tuxedo.

Most of the guests had a decent enough time that night. The oyster bar was fully stocked, and the champagne was flowing. But trouble lurked. After the party, Berringer went back to his desk at the other side of the office complex to tidy up some unfinished business, never mind how late it was. He was discovered the next morning, sitting at his desk, with two gunshot wounds in his chest. He was as dead as a smelt. The time of his death was later estimated to be between 12:00 midnight and 2:00 a.m., Mountain Time.

The most curious aspect of the crime scene was a note that Berringer had left on the pink notepad on his desk. The note said simply: "1:30 hence…," then it trailed off. The note had presumably been written after the shots were fired, in the limited amount of time that he had remaining.

Because Berringer's five school buddies were the last people to leave the party, they were considered the primary suspects. It turned out that four of them had gone out after the party, and each could vouch for the others' whereabouts. When told about Berringer's note, they confirmed that they were still together at 1:30. The only exception was Jimmie Wu, who didn't like the idea of all-night carousing, given that

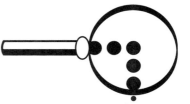

he was supposed to be a stern, proper official for the community. Wu insisted that he had gone straight to bed, but he had no one who could corroborate his story.

When Inspector Forsooth visited the crime scene, he looked up at the wall outside Berringer's office. There, through the glass, he saw a row of clocks, each displaying the time at one of Berringer Imports' offices around the world. First there was a clock labeled "Chicago," which was Berringer's first office outside of Bogusville. The row continued with the other six office sites, in order of their establishment: Paris, Los Angeles, Cairo, Mexico City, Caracas, and New York. Berringer liked to be able to look up from his office and see immediately what the time was throughout his empire. That way he could keep even better tabs on all his regional managers, all of whom he lorded over like a drill sergeant.

Forsooth studied the clocks as if in a trance, until one of the other detectives interrupted him. "Inspector, you okay?" Forsooth nodded. The detective then asked, "Any idea how we're going to locate the killer?" There was a short pause, and then Forsooth issued a curiously short reply: "Time will tell."

1) Who killed Bruce Berringer?

2) How can the other suspects be ruled out?

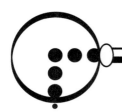

INSPECTOR FORSOOTH ANSWERS YOUR QUESTIONS

Q1—Were the clocks digital or analog?

They were analog. Had the clocks been digital, the killer might still be loose! (Remember, all the questions are actual questions from online sleuths. They didn't have the benefit of the illustration at the beginning of this story!)

Q2—If the high school cronies hated Berringer, why were they at the party?

Because Berringer was a vindictive, petty man, and there was no telling what he might do if they didn't show up to admire his wealth. Better to grin and bear it through one night.

Q3—Did it matter that Berringer's father was in the Navy?

Yes. It meant that Berringer was familiar with the concept of a distress signal, which is precisely what he was trying to convey in his note.

Q4—Was the murder committed at 1:30?
No, it was not.

Q5—Is the order of the clocks important?

Absolutely. Theoretically, though, you could deduce the answer without knowing the order!

Q6—Is the number of clocks important?

Even more important than the order, in some sense. The fact that there were seven clocks is central to the solution.

Q7—Were the clocks arranged in some sort of code?

They sure were. Semaphore code, to be precise, which Berringer probably picked up from his father.

Q8—Do you need to know semaphore code to be able to solve the mystery?

No, you do not—would I do that to you? All you need to know is

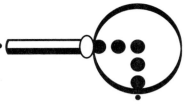

that semaphore code is given using flags and different positions of the arms—much like the hands of a clock. Each letter of the alphabet can be depicted by a specific position of the flags—or hands, as the case may be.

Q9—Dowling and Walters are the only two suspects whose names have seven letters. Does this mean one of them killed Bruce Berringer?
Believe it or not, the length of their names is not important.

Q10—Is the location of the offices important?
In general, no. But the location of a couple of them can lead you to the murderer.

Q11—When did the murder actually take place?
The murder took place at just after midnight. The "hence" in Berringer's note meant "in the future," not "therefore." You could use semaphore code to determine the precise time!

Q12—Is it significant that Berringer addressed Walters as "Maître d' "?
Yes, it's extremely significant. Remember, Berringer cared more about what people did than who they were. But in order to identify the killer, you're still going to have to supply one teensy-weensy ingredient that hasn't been covered in these 12 questions.

Can you solve the mystery?

Solution on page 165

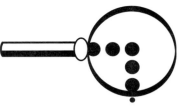

WARM-BLOODED MURDER

WHEN THE VOTES HAD BEEN COUNTED in the New Hampshire Republican primary of 1996, you could see the usual assortment of reactions: Pat Buchanan was rejoicing in victory, Bob Dole was putting the best spin on the slender margin of his defeat, and so on, from Steve Forbes and Lamar Alexander all the way down to the unheralded Michael Doucette.

But for the residents of Jasper Falls, New Hampshire, the day's political events were overshadowed by the stunning announcement that local political operative Vince Fernald, a mainstream Republican, had been bludgeoned to death. Jasper Falls was located not far from Dixville Notch, which had become famous for its position as the first town in the nation to get up and vote on Election Day. So politics were a pretty serious business in that neck of the woods, and getting more serious all the time.

Fernald's body had been found in a trash dumpster behind the town hall. The town hall served as a polling place for the community, and the small patch of land in back happened to abut Fernald's own backyard. His body was discovered late in the afternoon by a man named Clem Woolsey, a state employee who ran the garbage collection service for all the towns in the area. Tuesday was his regular day to service Jasper Falls, but in this case he had come to vote. In deference to the nature of his job, Woolsey had gone home and cleaned up after work that day, but once he got to the town hall he couldn't resist sneaking a peek in back to see how much trash was accumulating. To his horror, he noticed a foot sticking out of the dumpster, and when he summoned help to probe further, Fernald's scantily clad corpse was uncovered. Fernald's head had been struck several times, and a pool of blood had collected on one of the trash bags beneath his body.

In the wake of this grisly discovery, some curious facts emerged. One was that Fernald's overcoat was found in a park several miles from the murder site. The other curiosity was that candidate Michael Doucette, although winning less than one percent of the statewide vote, had

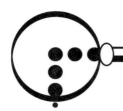

received almost twenty percent of the vote in Jasper Falls! Something very fishy was going on.

Suspicion immediately fell on local Doucette supporters Hugh Livingston and Clancy McTigue, but both men appeared to have iron-clad alibis. Livingston had been campaigning in Manchester and Concord during the weekend, and had driven back up Tuesday morning to place his vote at one of the two temporary booths set up at the Jasper Falls town hall. He remained at the voting area holding a Doucette sign throughout the day, the only exception being when he went out by himself for a late lunch at Charlie's Diner. Livingston was known in town for his ardent conservative stances, and his man Doucette made Pat Buchanan look like Jerry Brown. But as fearsome as Livingston was politically, it wasn't at all clear that a killer lurked inside.

As for McTigue, he had been in Jasper Falls trying to drum up local support for Doucette in the days before the primary. McTigue noted that he had been at the town hall practically all of Election Day. When asked about lunch, he said that he, too, had gone to Charlie's Diner. Unlike Livingston, however, he had eaten with several other Doucette supporters, any one of whom could attest to his whereabouts. After lunch, he went directly to the town hall to place his vote, and remained there afterwards.

Suspicion was also cast on a stranger in town, a reporter named Luc Evans-Wood, who lived well away from Jasper Falls. Evans-Wood said he had driven down the previous night in order to cover the primaries for his town newspaper. He also said the assignment had come at the last minute, so he had to sleep in his car. When asked whether it wasn't too cold to stay outside, he replied that he was a hardy soul, and he had been warned beforehand that the temperatures weren't apt to exceed five degrees. In his car was found an article praising Michael Doucette, but Evans-Wood said the article had been mailed to him, and it just happened to have arrived the day before. He admitted to being politically conservative, but denied any interest in Doucette or any personal stake in the outcome of the election.

Finally, Clem Woolsey, the man who had discovered Fernald's body in the first place, was told that he had been seen earlier that day driving his trash truck near the area where the dead man's coat had been found. Woolsey didn't seem surprised, and claimed that his appearance there

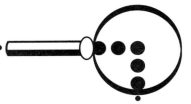

was consistent with his trash pickup schedule, although he acknowledged that it was two towns over from Jasper Falls. Woolsey also claimed that he had voted for Bob Dole, and was just as frustrated as other Dole supporters concerning their candidate's unusually poor showing in Jasper Falls. The Dole group protested that the election had been rigged, but there was never any evidence to support that claim.

When the authorities had the chance to review the case, they concluded that the most likely reason Vince Fernald had been killed was that he had simply been in the wrong place at the wrong time. But you must go a step further. Here are the questions you must answer:

1) Who killed Vince Fernald and why?

2) What are the alibis for the other suspects?

3) How did an examination of the voting records help the investigation?

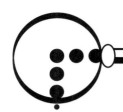

INSPECTOR FORSOOTH ANSWERS YOUR QUESTIONS

Q1—Did Jasper Falls have a regular trash pickup that day, considering that it was an election day?

Good question, and I hope I don't mislead you with my response. The answer is that on a primary day, work goes on as usual. It's up to employers to understand that people need to vote.

Q2—Is the timing of the primary important?

It sure is. It's pretty much impossible to make all the details fit without knowing when (calendar-wise) the crime occurred.

Q3—Did Fernald discover that votes were being tampered with?

It certainly looks as though he came across some high jinks at the town hall. It's a reasonable assumption that his discovery led to his murder.

Q4—Had Clem already serviced Jasper Falls prior to going to vote?

I love this question. It's another one that I hope I answer properly, without any misleading. But the answer is no.

Q5—Within the voting, are the candidates listed in alphabetical order?

Yes, they are.

Q6—The text refers to a "pool of blood" in the dumpster. Does this mean that it wasn't frozen? Is this an important detail?

The blood was most definitely not frozen. Is this an important detail? Well, it does seem to relate to the issue of how long the body had been in the dumpster. Let's just say that you're going to have to account for this issue in your solution!

Q7—But the mystery indicates that Clem had finished his work that day. How do you explain the fact that he hadn't gotten to the town hall dumpster?

One possibility is that the body was dumped off after Clem finished his rounds. But there is another, even better possibility that you should be thinking of.

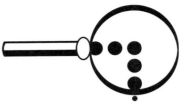

Q8—Did Luc Evans-Wood cast a vote that day?

No. I can say with complete certainty that Luc did not cast a vote that day, either in Jasper Falls or anywhere else.

Q9—What date was the murder?

Tuesday, February 20, 1996. That was the date of the 1996 New Hampshire primary.

Q10—If it was only five degrees out, how was Evans-Wood able to spend the night in his car?

Well, remember that he is the one who gave us the temperature in the first place. A very important fact!

Q11—Was the work week delayed because of President's Day?

Bingo. That's why the timing of the murder is so important. In fact, now we know a little bit more about the timing!

Q12—If the murder occurred the day after President's Day, how could Evans-Wood have received a letter the day before? Isn't he lying?

Not necessarily. Note that he had driven "down" to cover the primaries. When you consider that Dixville Notch—and therefore Jasper Falls—are in northernmost New Hampshire, you should see what I'm driving at.

Can you solve the mystery?

Solution on page 167

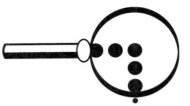

HALLOWEEN HORROR

BEING A GHOST FOR HALLOWEEN IS one thing. Becoming a ghost is another. But that's what happened to one teenage girl on this scariest of Halloweens.

The trick-or-treating part of the evening went about as expected, with house after house trembling as her wispy figure made its way up the front steps. The ghost lived in a town where folks took their costumes seriously, and people were especially generous to inspired creations. By the time the night was through, she had amassed enough goodies to last her until Thanksgiving. But she didn't last even one day, thanks to a fatal choice of late-night snack.

In the ghost's possession at the time of her death was a half-eaten Butterfinger bar, which was immediately sent to the toxicology lab. The results showed that the candy bar had been laced with rat poison: it must have been doctored and rewrapped, but the ghost never noticed it. But even if the question of how she died could be resolved, it wasn't at all clear who might have wanted her out of the way.

In real life, the ghost was in junior high school. She was a good student, seemingly without an enemy in the world. She was also a shoo-in to make the cheerleading squad for the upcoming basketball season. And with that small fact, a motive began to take shape. The problem was that the candy bar could have come from virtually anybody along her Halloween route.

The ghost's route on her final Halloween journey was painstakingly retraced, and some curious facts turned up: For one, she had been trick-or-treating with a group of friends until fairly late in the evening, and all were pretty sure that the ghost hadn't picked up any Butterfinger bars during their escapades. But after leaving her friends, she had gone to four houses in a final circle near her own home. And of those four families, three of them had a daughter who was vying for the same cheerleading squad! The families in question were the Ackmans, the Bartosavages, and the Claxtons, whom the ghost visited in that order. Her final stop came at Old Lady MacDonald's house up on the hill; the old lady was a widow, and her kids had all grown up and moved away.

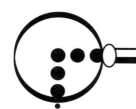

The interviews with these residents left the police no closer than they had been at first. Everyone professed outrage at the heinous Halloween crime that had shaken the neighborhood. Each said that the ghost was one of the last trick-or-treaters they had had that night (the earlier part of the evening having been taken up with younger kids), and each of them fiercely denied an attempt to poison for the sake of cheerleading—although they had all heard stories about such overzealous parents.

Not wanting to miss any detail, the police compiled records of how everyone was disguised that night. It turned out that Mr. Ackman had greeted his arrivals in his customary devil suit. Mrs. Bartosavage had greeted her callers in a light-up skeleton costume whose bones glowed in the dark. Mr. Claxton had devised a special outfit in which a woman's mask, etc., were placed on his back, so that he approached his guests facing backwards! When he turned around, the effect was creepy indeed. And Old Lady MacDonald, who was approaching 80 years of age, rose to the occasion by simply taking out her dentures and painting her face green. That, coupled with a mole or two on her cheek, made her the scariest witch of the night.

Of these four houses, only two—the Ackmans and the Bartosavages—had any Butterfinger bars remaining from Halloween. The ones they had left over were tested for rat poison, but those tests all came back negative. As for the Claxtons, they claimed to have treated visitors with many other items—M&M's, Hershey's, and Mars bars, among others. As for Mrs. MacDonald, she was known to be the least generous of all the neighborhood stops, and she only had licorice and saltwater taffy, which some trick-or-treaters suspected had been left over from the previous year!

One question that puzzled the investigators was that there had been two other girls who paraded through the neighborhood just before the ghost came. The first had been dressed as Mary Poppins. The second—wouldn't you know it—came dressed as a cheerleader. And both of them were trying out for the cheerleading team in real life. The existence of these two girls threw a monkey wrench into the entire investigation, because it wasn't clear whether the ghost had been singled out, or whether the killer would have been happy to knock anyone off just to create one more space on the squad.

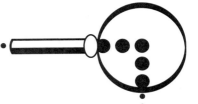

However, Inspector Forsooth thought it extremely likely that the ghost had in fact been singled out of the crowd. Acting on the assumption, he was able to identify the perpetrator.

1) Who killed the ghost?

2) How could the killer feel confident that no one other than the intended victim would be killed by the poison?

3) How did the killer's choice of costume play a role?

INSPECTOR FORSOOTH ANSWERS YOUR QUESTIONS

Q1—Was the victim still wearing her costume when she died?
No, she was not wearing her costume.

Q2—How did the killer know who the ghost was?
The killer found out through the grapevine, meaning that there was discussion about who was dressing up as what, so the ghost's identity was known in advance.

Q3—Was there anyone else dressed as a ghost that night?
Not in that neighborhood, no.

Q4—How did they know she would pick that particular Butterfinger bar?
It was the only Butterfinger bar there!

Q5—Did any of the people in the suspect houses know that the victim was coming by?
No. They had no idea who was coming until they got there.

Q6—Does the fact that the ghost left her friends to go alone have any significance?
Yes, it is quite significant. Had the ghost not gone out alone, there could never have been any assurance that she would pick up the tainted bar.

Q7—Was it important that the ghost was one of the last trick-or-treaters?

It sure was.

Q8—Did the ghost choose her own candy, or was it handed to her?

Great question. The ghost chose her own candy.

Q9—Were Butterfingers the victim's favorite candy bar?

No, they weren't necessarily her favorite, but they were certainly preferable to other choices.

Q10—So the widow, who had bad candy, wanted the cheerleader dead, and she put a good candy in the bad candy?

I didn't say that! What motive could she possibly have had?

Q11—What do Mrs. MacDonald's teeth have to do with it?

Well, remember that the killer wasn't taking any chances that the poisoned Butterfinger bar might end up in the wrong hands—or mouth.

Q12—Did the Mary Poppins carry an umbrella?

Sure did. And you're on the right track—but it looks as though you have to dig a little deeper.

Can you solve the mystery?

Solution on page 169

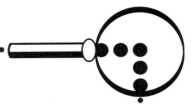

THE PRINTS OF LIGHTNESS

AFTER IT WAS ALL OVER, the workmen outside Oscar Delahanty's home could barely comprehend the irony of what had just taken place. The men had arrived promptly at 8:30 one summer morning to install a roadside fire hydrant some fifty feet or so from Delahanty's front walkway. Barely an hour into their job, well before the new hydrant was operational, they saw smoke billowing out of a first-floor window. They contacted their buddies at the fire department, who got down as quickly as they could. However, by the time the firefighters arrived, Delahanty's small but historic home had already sustained significant damage. And that wasn't all.

When the firemen on the scene trudged upstairs to Delahanty's bedroom, they found him lying in bed, quite dead. He was still dressed in his blue silk pajamas, so clearly he hadn't enjoyed much of this sultry summer morning. The fire itself hadn't reached the upstairs, but there was plenty of smoke all around. The firemen couldn't help but notice that the window in his bedroom, which looked out onto the road, was firmly shut.

The blaze had apparently started near the back door, which was part of the "newer" section of the house. By the looks of things, the hardwood floors in that area, including the back staircase, had just been refinished, but they had been almost completely torched by the blaze. Officials couldn't be certain just what had been used to ignite the fire, but they doubted that it had started by accident.

The fire chief noted that everything in the house seemed to be in compliance with local regulations. However, he couldn't help but note that older houses were notoriously great fire risks, and an alarm system that was directly wired into the fire department would have saved time and prevented some of the damage they were witnessing. Implicit in his remark was that a better system might have saved Delahanty's life.

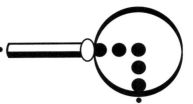

The next step was to alert Delahanty's employees at The Clip Joint, the hair salon he had owned and operated for just over six years. When the authorities got there, they could see that it was a busy morning, rendered all the busier by the boss's no-show. The three stylists on the job were Ginger LaCroix, Stan Norton, and Mitchell Quinn, each of whom had worked for Delahanty since the salon opened. When told that their boss had died of asphyxia, all three were momentarily speechless. After this stunned silence was over, Quinn said he would phone the boss's other appointments and officially cancel them. Ginger LaCroix had already placed a call to Delahanty's home, but had gotten only his answering machine. She asked if the house was damaged in the fire, and expressed relief that it could possibly be rebuilt. As for Stan Norton, he had apparently been planning on visiting the boss's home himself to see what was wrong, but now he did not have to.

The investigators took careful note of these various reactions, but it wasn't until 24 hours had elapsed that a possible motive appeared. A woman named Hilda Graylock came forward to say that Delahanty had offered her a job as a stylist with his salon. He had indicated to her that he was planning on letting one of his staff go, but she didn't know which one. To make matters even more interesting, not long after Graylock gave her testimony, another woman appeared at the police station and gave the exact same story! These tidbits certainly changed the complexion of things, and, upon consultation with the medical examiner, police now concluded definitively that Delahanty had been murdered.

Upon returning to the salon, the authorities picked up some more information about what had happened that morning. Mitchell Quinn testified that he had opened up the salon at 8:00 a.m. It was The Clip Joint's policy to rotate the responsibility for the 8:00 shift; the rest of the staff would come in later in the morning, well in time for the lunchtime crunch. The salon stayed open until 8:30 at night, and the bulk of its business was conducted at lunchtime and during evening hours.

As it happened, everyone had worked late the night before Delahanty's death. LaCroix and Norton had gone out for a drink and a bite to eat afterwards; they were joined by a couple from the massage studio located right next to The Clip Joint. That little gathering didn't break up until about midnight, whereupon everybody went home.

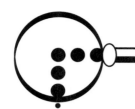

As for the next morning, LaCroix had come in about 9:30, while Norton had arrived a couple of minutes past ten, something of an annoyance to his 10:00 appointment.

A revisiting of the crime scene offered a couple of important details. Ordinarily, the back door to Delahanty's home would have been locked with a dead bolt, which was of course activated from the inside. But whoever had done the floor work had exited that way, and was unable to lock the door on the way out! So that explained how the killer could have entered the home without forced entry and without the workmen seeing him or her. Because of the layout of the house, it would have been quite easy for someone to have entered the back way without being spotted.

Upon hearing this crucial piece of information, Hilda Graylock lamented Delahanty's bad luck. He had evidently sought permission from the town clerk's office for several months to get the floors redone. (Because much of the house dated back to the early 18th century, it had attained landmark status, so he couldn't do much without the town's approval.) However, the "newer" wing, although still a century old, did not have quite the same restrictions, so the work was approved, as long as the wood was stained in a manner consistent with the rest of the woodwork. And just a day after the work was complete, Delahanty was dead.

Before authorities could get around to identifying the murderer, they received more than they could possibly have hoped for—a confession. That's right, one of Delahanty's employees admitted to having killed the boss. Ordinarily the investigation might have ended right then and there, but in this case the police truly got too much of a good thing. Later that same day, another Clip Joint employee admitted to having killed Delahanty! Neither confession could be readily dismissed. In fact, both people took lie detector tests, and they each passed with flying colors.

The bad news was that some important evidence had been destroyed. The good news was that the coroner's report turned out to invalidate one of the two confessions. Even without seeing that report, do you know who the real murderer was? Well, it's not easy, and a couple of issues will have to be resolved in the question-and-answer session that follows.

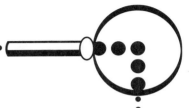

But here are the questions you must answer:

1) Who killed Oscar Delahanty?

2) Who wrongly confessed to the crime?

3) How did the coroner's report help identify the killer?

4) What was the "evidence" that was destroyed?

INSPECTOR FORSOOTH ANSWERS YOUR QUESTIONS

Q1—Could Ginger or Stan have killed him the prior night?
No. The folks at the massage studio could attest to their whereabouts all night.

Q2—Why is it important that Delahanty lived in a landmark house?
Because it wouldn't have been possible for him to have central air conditioning. (The fact that his bedroom window was closed suggests that there was no room air conditioner either.)

Q3—Since more than one person was being hired, does that mean that more than one person was being fired?
It certainly looks that way.

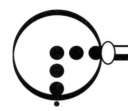

Q4—Did the floor refinishers leave the night before? If so, why didn't Delahanty check to make sure the doors were locked before going to bed?

The workmen had in fact left the night before, but they had essentially "painted in" the area near the back door, so Delahanty couldn't have gone in that area (i.e., to lock the door) without ruining the new finish.

Q5—Why was Ginger so concerned about the house?

Perhaps she had a sentimental streak, and didn't really like the idea of such a nice home being destroyed.

Q6—When the police said the victim had been "asphyxiated," does that mean that he died of smoke inhalation?

Not necessarily. "Asphyxiation" technically refers to any situation where breathing is impaired, whether arising from smoke inhalation, strangulation, or whatever.

Q7—Did the house's landmark status mean that it couldn't have smoke alarms?

Not at all. In fact, it was even more important for Delahanty to have smoke alarms, precisely because antique houses are extremely flammable. And the fire chief would certainly have noticed had Delahanty's smoke alarms been absent or defective.

Q8—Why was a hydrant being installed at that particular location?

Pure chance. Presumably the town had simply decided that it needed more hydrants, and noted that there wasn't one close enough to Oscar and his neighbors. (On a personal note, Inspector Forsooth returned home one evening to find a fire hydrant installed on the road alongside his own house. It does happen!)

Q9—Did the work on the hydrant begin that day or earlier?

Great question. The answer is that the work began that very morning.

Q10—If it was a sultry morning, why were Oscar's windows closed?

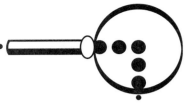

Another excellent question. We can assume that Delahanty wouldn't have been able to get to sleep that night had his window been closed.

Q11—Had the floor fully dried?

Given what we know about the weather, etc., it seems unlikely that the finish would have been perfectly dry. Some polyurethane finishes can take a full 24 hours to dry.

Q12—How many workmen does it take to install a fire hydrant?

No lightbulb jokes, please. The answer is that it takes several people to do the job, primarily because they have to jackhammer through the pavement to get to the pipes.

Can you solve the mystery?

Solution on page 170

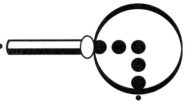

THE FINAL FORECLOSURE

IT WAS A SITUATION THAT HAD trouble written all over it. Niles Bronson was involved in the Ocean Towers condominium in every conceivable way: he had lived there since 1992, when the building was first constructed; he managed the condo fund, which covered all the routine expenses shared by the building's inhabitants; finally, he worked at Marine Bank, which held the mortgages on many of the condominium properties.

Several of Niles's colleagues on the condo board felt that he had conflicts of interest on the various matters that came before them. Others felt that he simply held too much influence, period. So when he was found dead in his living room one late-March evening in 1996, everyone figured it was an inside job.

No murder weapon was ever recovered, despite an immediate and exhaustive search of the entire condominium complex. But the suspicion of an "inside job" was only amplified when a search of the documents in Bronson's files revealed that three of the building's residents were facing foreclosure proceedings. That group consisted of Herman Gertner (like Bronson, a resident of Ocean Towers since its inception), real estate developer Graham Moss, and Jeff Carrington, who at one time had been a thriving restaurateur.

Each of the three men faced his own special type of financial distress. Carrington had been tracked down by his ex-wife and now faced substantial child support payments. Moss had leveraged himself to the hilt constructing an office building that was proving to be a dismal failure. And Gertner was withholding his mortgage payments until certain long-promised improvements were made to his property. Although the three men's predicaments were entirely different, what they had in common was that each had failed to meet his mortgage payments for several months. And that fact alone placed them under great scrutiny following the murder.

Actually, whoever killed Niles Bronson was lucky not to have been unmasked right away. A Mrs. Rose Kravitz, who lived in Suite 1507, just around the corner from Bronson's Suite 1516, claimed that she had

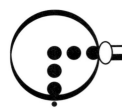

passed a strange man in the hallway as she took out the garbage late that afternoon. Ocean Towers was a fairly small, close-knit community; those on any particular floor tended to recognize those from the same floor, and this man simply didn't belong. At the time, though, Rose didn't think much about the stranger, nor did she get a good look at him. All she remembered was that he was wearing a T-shirt and some cut-off blue jeans.

The same evening, Rose had some business to discuss with Niles Bronson, and she was perplexed when he didn't answer her knock—hadn't he said he would be in? She said that she had made sure to knock at halftime of the NCAA semifinal game between UMass and Kentucky, in order not to catch him at a bad time. She could hear the TV from outside, though, and became suspicious when her repeated knocks brought nothing. She waited until the game was over, at which point she renewed her efforts and finally called the building superintendent, Win Scheinblum. Scheinblum opened the door to find Bronson's body on the floor, not far from his TV set. "Tales from the Crypt" was blaring in the background. It was evident that Bronson had been stabbed, but there was no sign of any weapon. It was only then that Rose Kravitz remembered the strange man and wondered whether he might have been involved.

However, just two nights after Bronson's murder, mayhem turned to madness in the form of another tragedy at Ocean Towers. None other than Herman Gertner was found lying on the busy walkway in front of the building, having apparently fallen from his balcony. He was alive, but just barely. He remained unconscious, unable to shed any light on what had happened to him, and hopes for his recovery were dim indeed.

As you might expect, when all else failed, Inspector Forsooth was called in to investigate. Forsooth went first to Herman Gertner's condo. He found the door to the outside balcony still open. The balcony had a three-foot-high protective metal railing, but several of its screws had come loose, and it wasn't sturdy enough to prevent the tragedy. Next came the Bronson murder scene. Nothing had been touched since the murder, except that the TV had been turned off and, of course, the body had been removed. A search for fingerprints had come up empty. Forsooth then proceeded to Graham Moss's apartment. Surprisingly, Moss was nothing short of ecstatic. He had just lined up a large

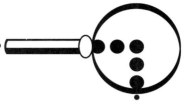

accounting firm to lease several floors of his faltering office building, and he relished the thought that his financial problems might be solved after all.

When Forsooth then spoke to the security personnel at the front desk, they confirmed that all three men on the foreclosure list had been on the premises for most of the day of Bronson's murder. Jeff Carrington had been out that morning, but he returned at about 2:00 p.m. and they didn't see him afterwards. They did see Graham Moss, who left at about 7:00 p.m. for a dinner engagement. And Herman Gertner left at about 8:00 p.m. to go bowling.

Forsooth's final stop was to interview Jeff Carrington, whose apartment was the most splendid of them all. Carrington admitted that he had gotten caught up in a free wheeling, free spending lifestyle, but it was now time to reform. He was trying to work out suitable arrangements to pay child support on time, but he conceded that staying at Ocean Towers was probably out of the question. He did ask how Herman Gertner was doing, and it was inspector Forsooth's sad duty to inform him that Gertner had not survived his fall.

On his way out, Forsooth ran into none other than Rose Kravitz, who admitted that some morbid fascination had made her decide to go out and gawk at the mark on the pavement where Gertner had landed. She also admitted that she wondered whether he might have been the man she saw on Saturday, right about the time that Niles Bronson was killed.

But Forsooth didn't think so. In fact, it didn't take long for him to realize that there had been a conspiracy to kill Niles Bronson—one that involved two of our three suspects. And he knew precisely how they worked together. Do you?

1) Who killed Niles Bronson?

2) What was the role of the accomplice?

3) Who killed Herman Gertner and why?

INSPECTOR FORSOOTH ANSWERS YOUR QUESTIONS

Q1—What do we know about the motive for Bronson's murder?

We have to assume that considerable ill will had built up between Bronson and one of the men being foreclosed.

Q2—Does what the man in the hallway was wearing mean anything?

Actually, it does. His attire suggests that he wasn't hiding anything on his person.

Q3—Why were the killers "lucky not to have been unmasked right away?"

All that meant is that if Rose Kravitz had gotten a better look, she might have been able to positively ID him.

Q4—Did "Tales from the Crypt" come on directly after the game, that is, on the same channel?

No, it did not. "Tales from the Crypt" was on FOX, whereas the NCAA games were on CBS.

Q5—What was the time of the fatal attack on Bronson?

Well, my previous answer actually gives something of a clue. Remember, Bronson was a big basketball fan and wouldn't have missed those games for the world.

Q6—What floor did Gertner live on?

I'm not sure of the exact floor, but there's an important inference available here, one that's quite relevant to the solution.

Q7—What kinds of repair needed to be done to Gertner's condo?

Wouldn't you know it? His balcony needed repairing. Gertner felt that it was dangerous, and it looks as though he was right.

Q8—When do they fire up the incinerator?

Well, in this day and age, Ocean Towers didn't have an incinerator. But trash disposal is a vital ingredient to this crime, that's for sure!

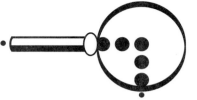

Q9—Why wasn't the work done on Gertner's condo?

He always felt it was because he wasn't as wealthy as some of the other occupants of the building and therefore didn't carry as much clout.

Q10—Did it matter that Carrington's condo was the most splendid of them all?

Actually, in a curious way, that fact is a nice little clue, once you think about the various factors that can make an oceanfront condo splendid.

Q11—Is there an exit to the building that doesn't go by the security personnel?

No, there isn't.

Q12—Was the murder weapon dropped down an incinerator shaft?

Great question! The incinerator part has already been covered, but the shaft is a great place to look. Remember, though, the garbage area in the basement was thoroughly inspected, and they didn't come up with a murder weapon.

Can you solve the mystery?

Solution on page 171

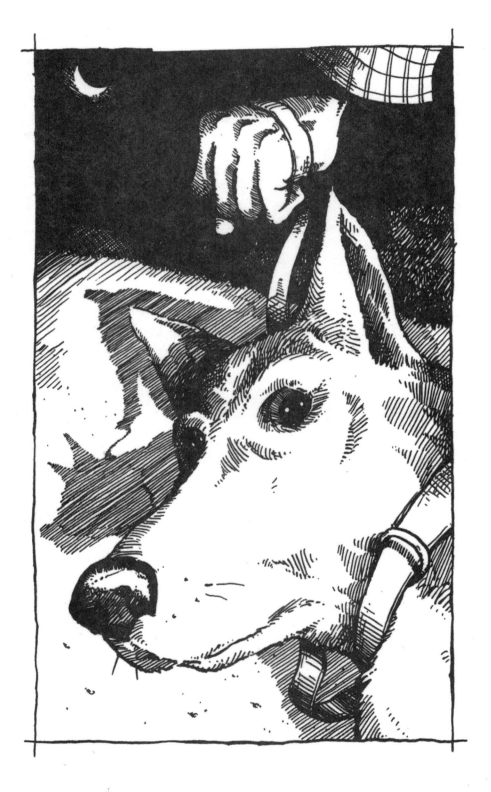

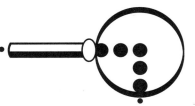

A TRAIL OF TWO CITIES

EVERYTHING ABOUT MELBA HOOGSTRATTEN'S DEATH was suspicious, from the method to the timing. Melba was a professor of English at the University of Portland, a position she had held for many years. But even a tenured professor's salary wasn't enough to satisfy her expensive lifestyle, so she established a part-time venture that had years of glory but may have led to her undoing.

The venture was a door-to-door bookselling operation called BooksAmerica. The company's approach, as developed by Melba, was to have its salespeople canvass homeowners and obtain order lists, typically of books that weren't as well publicized as the best-sellers you'd find at the major chains. BooksAmerica would then buy in bulk to satisfy those orders, which were fulfilled directly from publishers' warehouses. This way, the company obtained books at low prices and never had to worry about carrying inventory or paying for retail space. Meanwhile, publishers were delighted to get at least something for their warehouse merchandise. BooksAmerica had started with a sales force of three people and now had several hundred in its fold. Everybody was happy.

Er, not quite everybody. Things took a dark turn in the year before Melba's death. Clyde Finch, who had been the venture's very first door-to-door salesman working for Melba, didn't feel he was sharing in the company's profitability, and he threatened to set up his own organization, raiding much of BooksAmerica's sales force in the process by offering them more generous commissions. What made the situation especially difficult was that Finch had just been diagnosed as having pancreatic cancer: although still mobile and seemingly healthy, his doctors had given him no more than five months to live. Monte Trowbridge, Melba's lawyer and himself a partner in the book venture, suggested that Finch had decided to be spiteful to Melba as his one final act in life.

The other main partner of BooksAmerica was Esther Pogue, a colleague of Melba's at the university and an avid book reader. She was more sympathetic than Melba regarding Finch's unfortunate plight, but

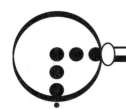

she was also distressed at his fiendish plot. The whole matter was extremely delicate, to be sure, and Pogue suggested that they call a meeting to discuss the future of the company.

The tension was particularly high in this meeting, in no small part because of Melba's conflicting attitudes. On the one hand, she was trying to pull away from the day-to-day operations of the company. She was entering a sabbatical year, and in a few weeks she would be teaching at another university, far away. Naturally she was going to be visited periodically by those close to her, but knew she needed a breath of fresh air.

On the other hand, Melba was understandably reluctant to lose any control of the business, especially if it wasn't on her own terms. Although the minutes of this fateful meeting were not available, a photograph of the main participants was, and that photograph later turned out to play an important role in the investigation.

Melba's death was a classic hit-and-run. The "accident" took place at night, while Melba was walking Foxy, her faithful German shepherd. A car sideswiped her from behind, and she was thrown to the ground along the side of the road. Foxy's frantic barking alerted one of Melba's neighbors, but by the time help arrived Melba had lost consciousness, and she never recovered.

An investigation of the prime suspects in the case revealed that not everyone could account for precisely where they were on the night of the murder. However, one alibi soon turned up out of nowhere. A man who lived in the same general area as Melba had his interest piqued when the newspapers released the now-infamous photograph of the principals (which, to review, were Melba, her advisor Monte Trowbridge, fellow professor Esther Pogue, and door-to-door salesman Clyde Finch).

The witness immediately called the authorities and advised that a solicitor had stopped by his house at almost precisely the time that Melba was killed, and that he was definitely the same man in the photograph. The witness also noted that the solicitor seemed perfectly calm as he went about his business—not the sort of reaction you'd expect from a murderer. Finally, the witness said he didn't notice any marks on the car, although he admitted that it was too far away for a good inspection.

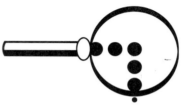

On the subject of possible stains, another surprise witness was an attendant at a nearby gas station, who swore that Monte Trowbridge had stopped by the station that night, at what turned out to be just minutes after Melba was run down. According to the attendant, the way the light of his service station shone down, he was able to get a very good look at the right portion of Trowbridge's front bumper, and swore that it was devoid of any markings. For his part, Trowbridge insisted that he had been with a client that night, and that he was completely innocent.

Esther Pogue noted that although people can sometimes make questionable eyewitnesses, dogs are more reliable. The reason she thought that important is that a day after the murder, she stopped by Melba's neighbor's house, where Foxy the German shepherd was being kept. As all who were present noted, the dog was completely friendly to Esther, even though her car was in plain sight. It was Pogue's opinion that Foxy would have reacted differently had he recognized her car as the murder vehicle.

Despite these various alibis, it was indeed possible to identify the murderer of Melba Hoogstratten. That, as you must surely know, is your very next task.

1) Which one of the suspects killed Melba Hoogstratten?

2) Indicate why the other suspects couldn't possibly have committed the crime.

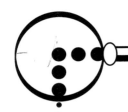

INSPECTOR FORSOOTH ANSWERS YOUR QUESTIONS

Q1—Was Melba killed before or after she left for her sabbatical?
That's the remarkable part about this mystery. We don't know the answer to this question, yet we can solve the murder anyway!

Q2—Who stood to benefit from Melba's death?
Presumably any of the principals in the firm would see his or her share increased if something happened to Melba.

Q3—Was Melba going to a place where they drive on the left side of the road?
She sure was. To England, in fact. (Hence the "Trail of Two Cities" title.)

Q4—Did the gas station attendant really see Monte Trowbridge?
You know, I can't say with complete certainty that he did. But we have to take his testimony at face value.

Q5—Could Esther have been driving a different car the night of the murder?
The car itself was the same, let's just say that.

Q6—Was the doctor's diagnosis regarding Clyde Finch correct?
Yes, sorry to say, it was correct.

Q7—Could Clyde Finch still drive despite his cancer?
Yes, he could. He can't be ruled out for that reason alone.

Q8—On what side of the street was the victim walking her dog?
If it was the U.S., she was on the right side. If it was the U.K., she was on the left. Simple as that.

Q9—The alibi provided by the neighbor described the attorney as a solicitor, an English term for lawyer. Why the difference in terms?

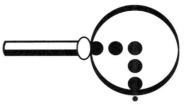

Ah, the question I've been waiting for. The answer is that the term "solicitor" would indeed refer to an attorney in the U.K., but would refer to something else in the United States.

Q10—Are dogs color blind?

It is widely believed that they are, but in reality they can distinguish between certain colors, such as red from blue, for example.

Q11—Was Clyde Finch alive when Melba was killed?

Not if she was in England! (It may seem unlikely, but there is a strong clue that might lead you to this important conclusion.)

Q12—Are there any issues with taking a dog to England?

There sure are. England is totally devoid of rabies, and they take special precautions to make sure that the disease is never transported into the country.

Can you solve the mystery?

Solution on page 173

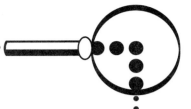

TIMING IS EVERYTHING

THE CASE STARTED OUT AS A ROBBERY but ended up as a homicide. On the face of it, that's not the strangest combination in the world. But in this case the person who was robbed wasn't the person who was murdered!

Early one Saturday morning, in the country town of Cedarville, a man named Buford Huxley reported that his toolshed had been broken into. The shed was secured by an ordinary combination lock that had been cleanly severed, probably with a pair of bolt cutters. The shed was located right outside Huxley's barn, and was where he kept all sorts of gardening tools—rakes, hoes, and the like. But most important of all was that he kept a set of hunting rifles there, and one of them was missing. That item was of particular interest to Inspector Forsooth upon his arrival that morning.

Forsooth knew something that Huxley might not have known. What Forsooth knew was that a man named James Hooligan, who lived about 30 minutes away, had been murdered just the night before by a rifle shot that came through the window of his home. And that set the stage for an interesting exchange.

Shortly after Forsooth arrived at Huxley's place, Muriel Huxley came out to the barn screaming, "Did you hear what happened?!" She had been listening to an all-news radio station while doing some gardening, and had heard the account of the murder. When she saw Forsooth, she backed off a bit, and he assumed it was because her hands and face were quite dirty; she apologized for her appearance, explaining that she had just finished planting some 300 daffodil bulbs along a stone wall behind their house. However, Forsooth wasn't too concerned with how she looked, because there was more to this story than met the eye.

Buford Huxley seemed strangely self-conscious upon hearing of Hooligan's death. It was clear that Hooligan was no stranger to this household, and the ties grew deeper as the investigation progressed. For one, the murder weapon was discovered in a wooded area about

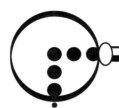

halfway between the Huxley and Hooligan residences. It was Huxley's missing rifle, all right, and ballistics tests confirmed that it was the source of the fatal shots. Separately, police uncovered a pair of slightly rusty bolt cutters not far from the rifle. Huxley admitted that the gun was his, but denied any part in the shooting. However, the Huxleys had to own up to some crucial and somewhat embarrassing facts upon further questioning.

According to Muriel Huxley, James Hooligan had been blackmailing her husband and two other men, Edgar Plotz and Dinky Martinez, for their participation in a kickback scheme several years before, when her husband worked for Acme Construction Company: Plotz and Martinez had given Huxley kickbacks in return for Huxley's selecting their then-struggling roofing company as a major subcontractor on projects spearheaded by Acme. Buford Huxley now worked with Plotz and Martinez in their own concrete-pouring venture, and part of the Huxley barn had been converted into an office for that venture. Hooligan had managed to figure out that the seed money for his new enterprise had come illegally.

Huxley at first denied the plot, but he conceded that he had received a threatening letter from Hooligan just days before. He also said that it was only a coincidence that the shed had been locked in the first place. He said he had gotten into an argument with his wife and obtained a lock so that she couldn't access her precious gardening tools—the rifles were the last things on his mind! He acknowledged that his two business partners were the only other people who even knew about the lock, but he was quick to add that he alone knew the combination.

The night of Hooligan's death, Huxley had held a meeting with his "coconspirators," Plotz and Martinez. The subject, of course: what to do about the blackmailing. Plotz had arrived at 8:45, Martinez at 9:00. The meeting lasted for about an hour, with no specific plan but a lot of anger and fear all around. Huxley admitted that his two friends had talked about giving Hooligan some "concrete boots," but he didn't take their bluster very seriously. Huxley also said that he had gone back to his house after the meeting. He assumed that the others had left immediately and hadn't come back, but he admitted that he wasn't sure. However, he could confirm that the lock was quite intact when he left the meeting.

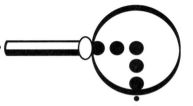

The coroner determined that James Hooligan had died sometime the prior night, but it wasn't possible to pinpoint the time of death any more than that. One potentially helpful detail came from one of Hooligan's neighbors, who had been walking her dog about 10:30. She reported that a light was on in Hooligan's downstairs bathroom, but as she walked by, that light went off. Interestingly, Hooligan's body was found in the downstairs den, whose window was right next to the bathroom window. The shot that killed Hooligan had been fired from the outside, as evidenced by a shattered windowpane and some glass fragments found in the den. When investigators arrived the next morning, the den light was still on, and the bathroom light was still off.

Dinky Martinez—who, despite his name, was a strong, stocky fellow—said he returned to his home at just before midnight, a time his wife confirmed. When asked what he did after the meeting broke up, he said that he had gone out to a neighborhood bar to shoot, er, play some pool. In fact, he had told his wife he'd been playing pool all night, to conceal the true nature of his business.

Edgar Plotz, the ringleader of the embezzlement scheme, claimed he had gone directly home after the meeting, arriving there at about 10:30. Because he lived alone, there was no one who could corroborate his story. He added that he didn't know a rifle from a bulb planter, but his lawyer cut him off before he could say more; now that the kickbacks were common knowledge, Plotz needed all the counsel he could get.

As for Huxley, he admitted that his wife was asleep when he got in after the meeting, so she couldn't vouch for him, but he insisted he didn't go anywhere.

Well, are you ready? Here are your questions:

1) Who killed James Hooligan?

2) Explain the key elements of timing in this case.

3) What was the missing piece of evidence that tied the murderer to the crime?

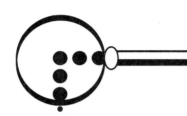

INSPECTOR FORSOOTH ANSWERS YOUR QUESTIONS

Q1—If the murder occurred after 10:30, would that implicate Dinky Martinez?

Yes, it sure would. Everyone else seems to have alibis for that time period, with the possible exception of Buford Huxley.

Q2—What time of year did the murder take place?

Presumably it was in the late fall, because Muriel Huxley was struggling to get all her daffodil bulbs planted before the ground froze. But the precise time of year isn't important.

Q3—Was the light hit by a shot from the rifle?

No, it wasn't. The only shots went through the window of the adjacent den. But knowing why the light went out would be very helpful regarding the timing of this case. Remember the title!

Q4—Was the murder related to the embezzlement?

Only indirectly. Sorry to be vague, but that's a clue in and of itself.

Q5—Would it have been possible for Buford Huxley to have gone to Hooligan's house without his wife's knowing?

Absolutely. She was sound asleep.

Q6—Could Muriel have cut the lock after the meeting ended?

No, for the same reason as the answer to #5 above.

Q7—Could Buford Huxley have cut the lock himself, to make it look as though someone were framing him?

It is entirely possible, although there is no evidence to back that up. Wouldn't that be clever?

Q8—Was the lock the same one bought by Huxley?

Yes, it was. Great question, though.

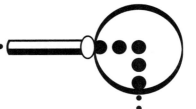

Q9—Was the murder actually announced on the radio?
It sure was. Muriel was entirely legit.

Q10—Had Plotz ever been inside the toolshed?
It sure looks that way, judging by his comment about the rifle and the bulb planter. As for when he might have been inside, well, that's something that your supersleuth abilities should figure out.

Q11—Was the neighbor certain about the time the light went out?
Positive.

Q12—Why were the bolt cutters rusty?
Because they had been outside longer than you might have thought.

Can you solve the mystery?

Solution on page 174

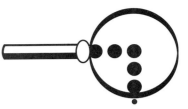

THE PIANO REQUITAL

AS GILBERT VON STADE PERFORMED, there wasn't an aficionado in the house who didn't marvel at his mastery of the keyboard. Von Stade was playing Chopin's Etude in G flat, Opus 10, no. 5, a most challenging piece by anyone's standards, even for a world-class pianist such as von Stade. The piece wasn't particularly long, as a number of performers were being showcased that night in a concert to benefit the city's sagging Foundation for the Arts. Yet it was a spellbinding few minutes.

When his work was done, von Stade got up from the piano to acknowledge a raucous standing ovation, which had become the norm at his performances. He was loved by virtually all who followed the music world; whereas other musicians of his talent tended to be aloof, he was known for being gracious and generous with his time. He took delight in the crowd, and always mingled after his concerts. But there was to be no mingling on this particular night. Against the backdrop of the applause, von Stade suddenly froze up and fell to the stage. The curtain was closed and the show came to a temporary halt. Gilbert von Stade would never regain consciousness.

At first, no one suspected foul play. Gilbert von Stade was a fairly old man, after all, and most everyone in the audience assumed that he had suffered a heart attack. Yet the autopsy would later reveal that his death was anything but natural. Traces of rare but deadly batrachotoxin were found in his system, and had surely been responsible for his death. It was murder, all right, but it remained to determine just who could have committed such a dastardly deed.

It turned out (surprise, surprise) that there was more to the decedent's true character than was ever seen by his adoring public. As is all too often the case within the highest echelon of musical talent, von Stade was an extremely demanding person to work with, and his own search for perfection often victimized those around him. Many thought him hypocritical for basking in the public glory of his music in the wake of exhausting practice sessions in which he had bullied and badgered everyone in sight.

Perhaps because of von Stade's preeminence, there was considerable friction within the group of musicians performing that night. Two younger pianists, Heinrich Albertson and Vivien Frechette, were also on the evening program, and were extremely eager to prove themselves. Albertson had come on before von Stade, and had given an absolutely flawless rendition of another Chopin etude: C major, Opus 10, no. 1. Frechette, on the other hand, was scheduled to play immediately following von Stade, but her performance was delayed by the onstage tragedy. In fact, some of those backstage had qualms about continuing the concert under the circumstances. Stage manager Sophia Brightwell, a frequent target of von Stade's tirades, tried to convince Frechette that it would be inappropriate for her to play, but Frechette would have none of it. She reminded them all that von Stade had been a professional, and had always lived up to the standard that the show must go on.

No one doubted that with von Stade out of the way, Albertson and Frechette had a better chance of success in their own musical careers. However, they certainly weren't the only suspects in the murder, for the rivalry had extended to the people in all of their lives, even if these very people had made a special effort that evening to heal all past wounds.

Marla Albertson, Beatrice von Stade, and Samuel Frechette never completely took to their positions as musicians' spouses. They were still very much in love with their respective mates, but they weren't necessarily attuned to their every note, so to speak. Marla Albertson was especially out of the loop, being unable to read sheet music, much less play it, but she had many other talents. One was cooking, and that night she had organized a pre-concert dinner, full of special culinary treats. She prepared frog's-leg appetizers, and encouraged others to make their own contributions. Samuel Frechette brought some homemade bread and Beatrice von Stade whipped up some linguine with pesto sauce. These offerings were joined by those from many other performers and their families, as the invitees included several dozen musicians who would play that night, not just pianists.

Although everyone applauded Marla for her initiative, the food selections weren't of universal appeal. Some of the musicians had no appetite because of pre-concert nerves, while others were reluctant to get too adventurous with their food choices while dressed in white tie.

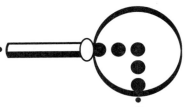

Among the pianists, only Gilbert von Stade was willing to handle greasy foods such as the frog's legs, but he made a special point of thoroughly washing his hands in the backstage men's room. On the subject of von Stade's food choices, a curious recollection of the evening's emcee, Walter Penwinkle, was that von Stade had garlic on his breath when he collapsed—on his dying breath, at that. Penwinkle and Sophia Brightwell had been the first people to rush to the stricken artist's aid, albeit in a futile cause.

After von Stade's death, the concert was delayed, but it resumed just minutes later with Vivien Frechette at the keyboard, playing Chopin's Etude in E flat minor, Opus 10, no. 6. The piece was slow and melancholy, if not downright mournful, a perfect choice under the circumstances. Then, in a tribute to von Stade, Frechette astonished all the spectators by playing the precise piece von Stade had played earlier. She, too, got a rousing ovation.

Some days later, Inspector Forsooth was called in to unravel the mystery of just what had happened during that ill-fated concert. He paid a visit to the stage where von Stade had fallen, and took time to survey the men's room in the back, where von Stade had washed his hands. There he found soap, toothpaste, mouthwash, some Breath-Assure tablets, and even a vial of DMSO, which Sophia Brightwell said von Stade used to take for his arthritis, before tiring of its side effects. Forsooth realized that the telling proof behind the von Stade killing might be hard to come by, but now he knew where to look.

1) Who killed Gilbert von Stade?

2) What was the method, and why did it work? Please be specific!

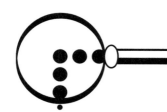

INSPECTOR FORSOOTH ANSWERS YOUR QUESTIONS

Q1—What is batrachotoxin?

Batrachotoxin is best known as the poison used by some South American tribes to coat their hunting arrows. The poison comes from the secretions of a certain species of tree frog. The natives dipped their arrows into the frog secretions, so even if the arrows didn't cause fatal wounds, the batrachotoxin would. (Not my style, but that's life in the jungle for you.)

Q2—Did Samuel Frechette bring garlic bread to dinner?
Nice try, but no. He brought plain bread.

Q3—How could a food poison get specifically to von Stade if the nonmusicians were eating some of everything?
Good question. I haven't the foggiest idea how that would be possible.

Q4—Does the linguine have garlic in it?
The linguine doesn't have any garlic in it, but the pesto sauce is loaded with it. However, there is a pretty good clue that this didn't kill von Stade.

Q5—Are the pieces played by the pianists relevant?
Yes, they are all relevant.

Q6—What were the unwanted side effects of DMSO?
Nice question. The answer is that von Stade detested the fact that DMSO left him with a garlicky taste in his mouth! (Yes, that's an actual side effect, and it was especially intolerable for von Stade, who liked to mingle with his adoring fans.)

Q7—Does Frechette play with gloves?
No, none of them played with gloves. Another nice question, though!

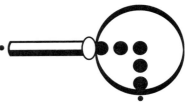

Q8—Could the pianist who played before him have put the poison onto the keys?

No, that would have been extremely difficult to do, because he was in plain view of the audience the whole time. We have to assume the poison was placed there just before the show began.

Q9—What was so difficult about von Stade's piece?

Ah, I was hoping you would ask. The answer is that the piece is more difficult because it's harder for the fingers to move around on the black keys, which are smaller!

Q10—Did everyone know that piece of music von Stade was playing that night?

Certainly all the musicians did, and everyone involved with the show did.

Q11—Could the toxin have been absorbed by the skin?

Sure could, if mixed with DMSO. One of the properties of DMSO is that it is readily absorbed through the skin, and in its liquid form is capable of carrying other compounds right along with it.

Q12—Is it possible that the victim was killed by accident, and that one of the other musicians was the actual target?

It's quite possible, and it's a great question. However, that wasn't the case, and it's our job to show how we know that.

Can you solve the mystery?

Solution on page 175

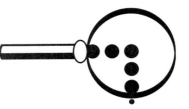

THE VALENTINE'S DAY MASSACRE

IT WAS ONLY AFTER RUDY MARCUS WAS KILLED that his community got a full taste of what his life was really like. Marcus seemed like your average, everyday, strait-laced, white-collar type. A CPA by training, he worked at the Ernst Brothers accounting firm, and by all indications had done quite well for himself.

He had the usual trappings—a nice car and a well-groomed house in the suburbs—all in keeping with his solid-citizen image. But there wasn't much flair to Rudy. Businesswise, Rudy's clients didn't hire him because of his imagination; they hired him for the decimal-point precision with which he approached life. At home, there hadn't been a Mrs. Marcus on the scene for several years. Most people figured she had simply gotten bored.

However, within days of the discovery of Rudy's body, the entire picture changed. One of his neighbors, a Mrs. Cecily Wheelock, revealed that Rudy Marcus was in fact a closet Romeo, a prim accountant by day but a freewheeling bon vivant by night. He was having dalliances with no fewer than three women at the time of his death, each one claiming to be Rudy's real girlfriend. Those three became the focus of an extensive murder investigation.

Fittingly, Rudy had been killed on Valentine's Day, and the murder scene was consistent with a classic crime of passion. Rudy's body lay on the kitchen floor with a knife in his back. The murder weapon was one of his own kitchen knives, which had been taken from its usual resting place on the magnetic rack. It appeared that someone had stabbed Rudy the Romeo when his back was turned. From the absence of a struggle, it was assumed that Rudy knew whomever had murdered him.

The first of Rudy's mistresses to emerge was Cornelia Devane, who worked at the Estee Lauder counter at the nearby Bloomingdale's. Ms. Devane said she had been seeing Rudy for over a year, and was shocked

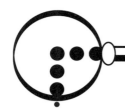

to find out that there could have been other women in his life. But as she reflected on their relationship, she realized that his availability was sporadic. She had always chalked his busy schedule up to work-related matters, but now she knew better.

Then there was Daphne Nagelson, who had met Rudy the old-fashioned way—as a tax client. She said she was absolutely convinced that Rudy loved her the most, and to prove it she brought out an emerald brooch he had given her for Valentine's Day. Rudy had bought the brooch while in South America a few months before.

The third of Rudy's girlfriends was Mary Stahl, the only one of the three who was married. She also happened to be a city councilwoman, a highly visible role. Yet no one around her knew of her relationship with Rudy. One interesting aspect of the case, which Stahl shed light on, was that Rudy had been in California on a business trip for several days prior to his murder. Originally he was supposed to have returned on the 12th, but his client needed more help than he had planned, so he didn't return until the 13th—just one day before he was killed.

Some of the investigators wrinkled their eyebrows upon hearing that little nugget. Apparently they figured that their dead little Casanova might have had something going in other ports as well, but that was never substantiated. Mary Stahl confirmed that Rudy had been thinking about her during his trip, as she brought out a gold necklace he had bought for her while he was away.

It turned out that Rudy had prevailed upon Cornelia Devane to visit his house periodically while he was gone. Her main task was to water the plants, but he also wanted her to turn some lights on and off to thwart any potential burglars, and even to watch TV to give the house a "lived-in" look. Devane said she had done that same routine many times in the past, and expressed some feeling that she had been taken for granted. Rudy hadn't called her while he was gone. However, he had unexpectedly stopped by her workplace on Valentine's Day to give her a present—a red silk scarf.

Daphne Nagelson told the police that she and Rudy had gone out to see the movie *Bed of Roses* the night before his death, and she produced the ticket stubs to prove it. Cecily Wheelock, the snoopy neighbor, said that Daphne had stopped by Rudy's house earlier on the 13th, and she didn't deny it. But she did deny having gone inside, saying that

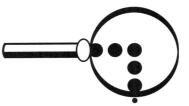

she'd just stopped by to drop off her Valentine present for Rudy. Mrs. Wheelock confirmed that Daphne had had a little smile on her face when she left the house.

According to the "rotation" that seemed to be developing, that left Mary Stahl as Rudy's companion on the fateful night of February 14th, and, sure enough, she admitted that they, too, had gone to see a movie. When pressed as to the title, she stammered *Dead Man Walking*, not liking the irony of the title one bit. The movie was her treat, so she also had ticket stubs to present, which indicated to the authorities that Rudy was still alive until at least 9:30 p.m., when the movie ended. The coroner had already estimated the time of death as being between 8:00 p.m. and 11:00 p.m., based on the preliminary examination of such factors as rigor mortis and eye fluids. So Rudy clearly didn't live very long after the movie. Stahl also admitted that she'd left a message on Rudy's answering machine the night before he came home. The police located that very message on the machine.

Just when it appeared that the investigation was at a standstill, Inspector Forsooth noted that based solely on the evidence they already had, there was strong reason to believe that one particular woman in Rudy's life had found out about at least one of the others. When the authorities went back to confront that woman, a confession resulted. Your job is to figure out who confessed.

1) Who killed Rudy Marcus?

2) Rudy's personality played a role in his demise, in two distinct ways. Name them.

3) The testimony of two particular people would prove very helpful in bringing the guilty party to justice. Which two?

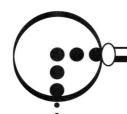

INSPECTOR FORSOOTH ANSWERS YOUR QUESTIONS

Q1—Is it proven that Mary and Rudy stayed for the whole movie?

They could have left early, but I believe they stayed for the whole thing.

Q2—Since Cornelia was housesitting for Rudy, did she intercept Mary's message on the answering machine?

We have to assume that if Cornelia was in the house, she heard the message, because he had an answering machine, not voice mail.

Q3—Did the gifts have anything to do with the murder?

They sure did, but not in the way you might think.

Q4—Which of the presents Rudy gave was the most valuable?

The emerald brooch was the most valuable, followed by the gold necklace. The red silk scarf was a distant third.

Q5—Was there any perfume scent noticed around the body?

There was a vague scent of perfume around the house, but it wasn't concentrated around the body. Sorry!

Q6—Did the police talk to Mary Stahl's husband?

No, they didn't. Actually, none of the questions asks for two witnesses who might be helpful. I can tell you right now that only one of them is named in the text, so Mr. Stahl is a good guess for the other. Alas, he's not the one.

Q7—How do you know that Daphne only went in the vestibule?

We have to take her word on that. Besides, she was only there a second or two, as Cecily Wheelock could confirm.

Q8—What was Daphne's gift? Was Rudy home when she delivered it?

I don't know what Daphne's gift was, and it really doesn't matter. But I can say that Rudy wasn't home when she delivered it. And his absence turns out to be extremely important in reaching the solution.

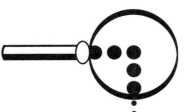

Q9—Where in the United States did the murder take place?

Believe it or not, it doesn't really matter. But we can assume from the language in the text that it took place outside of California, and that is important!

Q10—Is the fact that Rudy is an accountant significant?

Yes. He made a living out of reducing people's taxes, including his own. Income tax, state tax, sales tax—he hated them all. And that, believe it or not, is a big clue.

Q11—Was Cornelia angry at Rudy for not calling her while he was away?

Perhaps, but his failure to do so is good for her in a different sense, which is explained in the solution.

Q12—Where was Rudy when the package was delivered?

Rudy was not home when a particular package was delivered. (I hope that's not misleading!)

Can you solve the mystery?

Solution on page 177

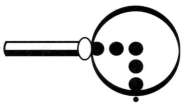

WHERE THERE'S A WILL

MARION WEBSTER WAS ONE OF THE MOST eccentric people ever to walk the planet. To him, communication was a game to be played for personal amusement, and nothing else. And when he died, everyone else was left to explain exactly what had happened. It wasn't easy.

The occasion was the 35th birthday party of Webster's eldest daughter, Laura. Each of his six children was able to make it home for the late-September festivities. Webster had three sons—Eugene, Herbert, and Biff—and three daughters—Laura, Gwen, and Dorothy. All were grown up, but none as yet had started families of their own, a fact that displeased Webster tremendously. As the family patriarch and himself a retired widower, he felt it was his role to push his children in every imaginable way, even if the results didn't always match his expectations. Unfortunately, he used his own will to reward or penalize his children's efforts. It was a fatal mistake.

Instead of simply dividing his estate equally, Webster had designated that each child would receive something consistent with his or her own interests. For example, Herbert, a struggling stockbroker, was to receive the bulk of his father's stock portfolio; Gwen, a budding socialite, was to receive a diamond necklace that had belonged to Webster's own mother. Dorothy, a librarian, was to receive Webster's extensive book collection. And so on.

The birthday weekend was filled with tension. At various times during their brief stay at Webster's Florida retreat, each of the children was summoned into the study to talk about their father's plans to reconfigure his will. The study was an imposing room, with a large oak desk in the middle and three of the four walls taken up by shelves housing his remarkable collection of reference works. It could be said that Webster's children lived in fear of their father. But tension gave way to tragedy early Sunday afternoon, when Marion Webster was found dead at his desk, the victim of a single gunshot wound to the chest.

As is so often the case, Inspector Forsooth wasn't called in until after the initial investigation had failed. One of the reasons for that failure was that none of the six children had much to say about Webster's

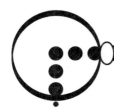

plans with his will. Said Biff, "Everything that Dad did or said was misinterpreted, unless you knew him awfully well. Me, I was born on April Fool's Day. Maybe I learned early that things aren't always what they seem."

What was known is that the murder occurred in the early afternoon, following lunch. Gwen had made the lunch, and Laura had prepared the dessert. After lunch, Laura, Dorothy, and Herbert were outside by the pool when they heard a shot ring out. They rushed into the study and found nothing except their father's dead body. The other family members then turned up in short order. But if anyone saw anything of great importance, they weren't saying so. As if this weren't frustrating enough, no murder weapon turned up, even though the investigators searched the rest of the house very carefully.

The only real evidence was a piece of paper found on Webster's desk that seemed to shed light on his intentions with his children. But the note contained only cryptic phrases:

I have decided to "rearrange" a portion of my will.

Bond portfolio is satisfactory—generates income.

Plan to decrease Gwen's inheritance will be put on ice.

Herb/pasta salad was commendable, and deserving of recognition. But a disappointment after that.

Finally, I've decided that book donations will be limited, but funding libraries will increase. (I'm sorry that signs got crossed.)

Inspector Forsooth, after getting used to Webster's strange method of communication, was able to solve the case and obtain a confession. He was also able to determine what happened to the murder weapon by concluding that the killer must have returned to the crime scene during a lull in the first, sloppy investigation. With that in mind, here are your questions:

1) Who killed Marion Webster?

2) Where was the murder weapon hidden after the crime?

3) Which of the children was Webster going to treat harshly in his revised will? (One of them is the killer!)

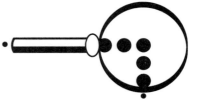

INSPECTOR FORSOOTH ANSWERS YOUR QUESTIONS

Q1—Why is "rearrange" in quotes?

Because "rear range" is the same thing as "back burner," meaning that some of the will was being left unchanged for now.

Q2—Does the "Herb" in Herb/pasta salad refer to Herbert?

Yes it does.

Q3—Was Webster referring to lunch when he said "a disappointment"?

No!

Q4—Was Webster the sort of guy who would change his will over a stupid dessert?

You never know with Webster, but one has to believe that he wasn't that strange.

Q5—Is there a distinction between a stock portfolio and a bond portfolio?

There sure is. The bond portfolio was not going to Herbert the stockbroker.

Q6—Why does Webster's note say "Bond portfolio is satisfactory—generates income"?

Because the name of the person who deserves the income is right there, if you look hard enough.

Q7—What was Eugene to inherit?

I think that question was just answered.

Q8—Is it important that Biff was born on April Fool's Day?

In an incredibly obscure way, yes.

Q9—Did they have pasta salad for lunch?

There is no evidence to suggest that they did.

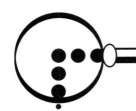

Q10—Was Herb's childhood commendable?

Apparently it was, and that's what Webster was trying to communicate. As I indicated in my prior answer, whether they actually had pasta salad for lunch is anyone's guess.

Q11—Does "signs" refer to signs of the zodiac?
Yes!

Q12—How many "losers" were there in Webster's revised will?

There were three. And remember, every one of Webster's children is accounted for in his cryptic notes!

Can you solve the mystery?

Solution on page 178

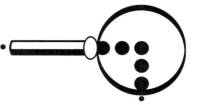

THE OVERHEAD SMASH

IT WAS NO ORDINARY U.S. OPEN, that's for sure. This one had a special excitement to it, what with political intrigue in the second week and some breathtaking tennis on the final weekend. But Manny Heitz never made it that far.

Heitz's body was discovered on Friday afternoon during the first week of the tournament. He was working as a linesman throughout the event, and had been scheduled to work two matches on that fateful day—an early-round singles match in the stadium at 11 a.m. and then a late-afternoon doubles match on the grandstand court. But when he didn't show up for the second match, tournament officials sent someone over to his house. Heitz's body was found in the kitchen of his home, not far from the tennis stadium. He was wearing his official U.S. Open outfit.

Heitz had been struck on the head, and the murder weapon wasn't especially difficult to find: his Wilson T2000 tennis racquet lay by his side, the top of its frame stained with blood. Closer examination revealed that there were several strands of hair stuck to the blood, hair that turned out to be Heitz's. The room bore the signs of a struggle, and it was therefore surmised that the death may have been accidental, in the sense that the perpetrator might have struck Heitz without intending to kill him. Either way, the coroner estimated that the time of death was between 12:00 and 2:00 in the afternoon. The autopsy also revealed two separate blows to Heitz's right temple, one of which may have been enough to have knocked him out, the other of which was presumed to have been fatal.

Interviews with other linespeople who worked that first match revealed that no one had any recollection that anything was wrong. However, it turned out that none of them really knew Manny Heitz in any real sense. They were focusing on calling their own lines, and not much else.

Of the people who actually knew the victim, one of the last to see him alive was Ernie Welch, who owned a sporting goods store in the area. Apparently Heitz had stopped by Welch's store early in the morn-

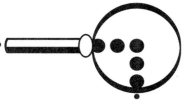

ing on the day of his death to buy a few tennis-related items—wrist bands, a pair of sneakers, and a couple of pairs of socks. Heitz wanted to look his best when he was on the stadium court.

According to Ernie Welch, the match that Heitz was going to be involved with at 11:00 was a big one, as early-rounders go: Tracy Molotov of the Soviet Union versus Chris de la Harpe of South Africa. The match was especially meaningful to Heitz because one of his frequent doubles partners, Wayne Melanson, was Molotov's agent, while another occasional partner, Roger Dant, was de la Harpe's cousin. Each of them had actually tried to bribe Heitz to make calls that were favorable to the player of their choice! At first Heitz thought they were joking, but Welch remembered warning him that he was underestimating their fanaticism.

What happened in the match was truly bizarre. Molotov, the favorite, was beaten by de la Harpe in one of the day's major upsets, in part because the side linesman called Molotov's patented slice serves wide on a couple of crucial break points, thereby taking away one of his most potent weapons. Molotov was absolutely convinced that the balls in question had skidded off the tape, and was livid when the umpire refused to overrule (as they so often decline to do). Molotov eventually lost his cool, and with it the match.

Another friend of the victim, a woman named Janet Stringfellow, had been in the stadium for that match. She later said that the emotions during those line-call arguments were so strained that she joked to a friend, to her later regret, that Heitz would be lucky to escape with his life! But she was on the other side of the court, well up in the stadium, and was unable to see the action very closely. In fact, she said that she had trouble distinguishing the two men who were playing! Apparently the match wasn't nearly as important to Stringfellow as to some of the others. She joked that she hadn't followed the game in a while, and probably wouldn't recognize any tennis players that weren't Jimmy Connors or Bjorn Borg! She also said that she spent the afternoon at the tournament, trying to reacquaint herself with the whole tennis scene.

Upon investigating Heitz's alleged buddies Roger Dant and Wayne Melanson, some interesting facts turned up. For one, Melanson was extremely upset by Molotov's early loss, because he thought his client had a chance of breaking through all the way to the semi-finals.

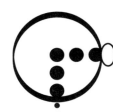

Melanson didn't see the de la Harpe match personally, but he admitted that early that afternoon, upon finding out about the controversy, he went to Heitz's place to confront him. However, he insisted that by the time he arrived, Heitz was already dead! Melanson left without telling anyone, fearful that someone would suspect his involvement. Investigators noted that Melanson was much bigger than Heitz, and would have had no trouble subduing him.

As for Dant, he said that he had watched the entire Molotov/de la Harpe match, and had then gone to the local public courts and picked up a game. He pointed to his scraped knee, an injury he said he incurred because the courts had not been watered recently and were therefore slippery. Dant also said he had a conversation with a woman who was admiring his "RACQUET" vanity license plate, which was easily visible because of the dark letters on the bright orange background. He said he talked to the woman for over 20 minutes before the pickup game started, and he remembered getting on the court at precisely 1:00 p.m. The authorities of course set out to confirm these various claims.

Upon piecing together all these bits of information, Inspector Forsooth was able to come up with the solution—your very next task. Here are the questions you must answer:

1) Who killed Manny Heitz? What was the murder scenario?

2) What was the crucial piece of evidence the killer tried to cover up? Why was his effort doomed to failure?

3) Let's suppose that this case came to trial. Although no one saw the crime committed except for the killer and the victim, name one person whom the prosecution would surely want to get as a witness for its side.

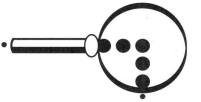

INSPECTOR FORSOOTH ANSWERS YOUR QUESTIONS

Q1—Is Molotov left-handed?

We can deduce that he is, yes, because his "patented slice serves" were called out on "crucial break points" by a "side linesman." Most break points in tennis arise in the so-called "ad court," where a slice serve is most effective for a left-hander because it brings the ball out wide (à la John McEnroe). However, given that Janet Stringfellow had trouble distinguishing between Molotov and de la Harpe, it follows that both of them are left-handed! (A lot of work for not much reward, wouldn't you say?)

Q2—Don't New York license plates have a white background?

They do now, but they weren't always like that.

Q3—What is the significance of the clothing that the dead man had bought?

Believe it or not, one specific item that Manny Heitz purchased is a big help in tracking down the killer.

Q4—Did Heitz live close to the National Tennis Center?

Hmmm. A good question. Heitz lived about 15 minutes by car from the National Tennis Center in Flushing Meadows, but that's a highly misleading answer!

Q5—The story says that Molotov was from the Soviet Union. Isn't that out-of-date?

No, it is not. And that's a useful clue, in and of itself.

Q6—What is the average length of a men's singles match at the U.S. Open?

It is fairly uncommon for three-out-of-five-set men's matches to take less than two hours, but there is a very good reason why this particular match was shorter than we might be accustomed to. Let's assume each set of the match took one hour. Okay?

Q7—When did New York State adopt its current license plates?

In 1976, the bicentennial year, New York made a patriotic move toward red, white, and blue plates. Prior to that time, the plates were orange with dark blue lettering.

Q8—Was Melanson angry at Heitz? Hadn't Heitz's calls cost Melanson a lot of money?

The answer to the first question is yes: he certainly was angry, at least for a while. The answer to the second question, technically, is no.

Q9—Why in the world was Heitz playing with a T2000? I thought they went out of style years ago!

You're right. They did. The Wilson T2000—the first steel racquet and for years the weapon of choice (so to speak) for one Jimmy Connors—was a revolutionary product but was also one of the worst racquets ever made! However, it was once in vogue.

Q10—Why is the sideline referred to as a "tape"?

Because the match in question was not being played on a hard court, in which case the term "line" would have sufficed.

Q11—Was Heitz wearing the new tennis shoes when he died?
He sure was.

Q12—Did Heitz make it to his 11:00 match?

No, he did not. But a sleuth of your skill had figured that out already, right?

Can you solve the mystery?

Solution on page 179

158

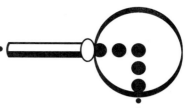

PIER FOR THE COURSE

INSPECTOR FORSOOTH'S FINAL CASE (for now) shows how dangerous it is to play with guns—especially when hard-core, aggressive corporate types are involved. The occasion of interest to us is the off-site meeting of the Fairport Firearms Company. For several years the firm's senior and middle managers had met at some unusual locales to bond, try out different management techniques, and ultimately to test the mettle of all those who attended. This time around, the group agreed to go on a hunting and fishing expedition at Lake Nineveh. It was a decision that permanently changed the company and the lives of those who worked for it.

The focus of the weekend was on three of the company's vice presidents, all of whom were extremely hungry for professional advancement: David Willoughby, the chief financial officer; Kevin Van Allen, the head of the sales division; and Paula Fine, the marketing director. Each of these three was the head of a corporate "team" for the off-site meeting. The reason this turned out to be important is that only the team leaders spent any time by themselves—everyone who worked under them was always in a group, with others to attest to their whereabouts. The three groups took turns occupying different areas of the lakeside, each of which offered its own special terrain. Although no hunting was done per se, everyone had real guns and blanks for use in the role-playing survival games that the teams were engaging in. The whole idea of the weekend was to create a primitive setting that would develop ingenuity and teamwork.

Tragedy struck at lunchtime on the second day of the meeting. Each employee had been given a box lunch containing a peanut-butter-and-jelly sandwich, potato chips, bottled water, and, finally, a caramel apple to celebrate the fall season. The only exception to the rule was senior vice president Wayne Metzger, the second-most-powerful person in the company; he was given a ham sandwich instead of the standby PB&J because of a longstanding and extremely serious allergy to peanut oil. Metzger and company president Bart Strunk were the only two who didn't participate in the management games that

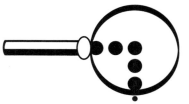

morning. Instead, they located themselves on a pier that jutted out into the lake, prepared to enjoy some relaxing trout fishing. But neither one made it off the pier alive.

The first people to reach the crime scene were David Willoughby and his assistant, Sharon Sturgis. In a sense, their appearance was surprising, because just prior to the lunch break Willoughby's group had been out at Rocky Point, the most remote locale of them all. But they wanted to see how the fishing was going—so they headed to the pier. They saw the bodies from a distance and ran toward them. Sturgis tried in vain to revive Metzger, who had collapsed for unknown reasons. Willoughby went farther out on the pier, where Bart Strunk lay dead. Strunk had been shot twice in the chest. Willoughby noted to his assistant that the two must have just finished their lunch, as the core of Strunk's caramel apple lay beside him, still white. Metzger's sandwich was finished, but he hadn't gotten to his apple yet. The bottled water, plastic cups, and potato chip bags were strewn around the pier. Clearly the men hadn't had a chance to clean up.

The other two groups—led by Kevin Van Allen and Paula Fine— were quickly called in, and the fun and games stopped right there. Because the woods had been resounding with fake gunfire throughout the day, no one could be sure exactly where the shots that hit Bart Strunk had come from, or, for that matter, when they had been fired. But the murder weapon was eventually fished out of the lake, not far from the pier. Fittingly, Strunk had been shot by one of his firm's own guns.

The search for clues began, and a number of interesting facts turned up. Some had to do with corporate intrigue at Fairport Firearms, such as the fact that Van Allen and Fine had a romantic relationship. They had tried to keep the relationship a secret, but they were caught red-handed on Lake Nineveh: when asked what they were doing during the time just before the discovery of the bodies, they had no choice but to admit that they had sneaked away for a romantic liaison in the woods. The two seemed embarrassed by the disclosure, but they realized that it would have looked much worse if they had been unable to account for their whereabouts. In any event, many people in the company had figured out that Van Allen and Fine had long-term plans for themselves as a couple, plans that included running Fairport Firearms one day.

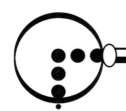

The odd man out among the three vice presidents was David Willoughby, who had a particularly close working relationship with the late Wayne Metzger. Metzger, as senior vice president, apparently treated Willoughby roughly, and took full use of the corporate power he held. However, Willoughby was also fiercely loyal to Metzger, and always saw to it that Metzger's personal quirks were satisfied. He figured that if Metzger was going to be running the show at some point, it made sense to play along.

As far as the off-site meeting went, the murder investigation confirmed some basic details. First of all, because there were so many extra guns around, the murder weapon could not be pinned on any one person or team. However, it was readily determined that the group led by Paula Fine had been in the area closest to the pier for the 20 minutes or so prior to the discovery of the bodies. Sturgis added that as part of standard procedure, she had double-checked Metzger's box lunch after Willoughby's initial check and didn't notice anything wrong with it.

Inspector Forsooth surveyed the evidence and came to a surprising conclusion—that the deaths had resulted from a two-person conspiracy! More than that, there was a twist at the end, because Forsooth claimed that one of the coconspirators had pulled a double-cross! Your job is to determine who spoiled the fun and games at Lake Nineveh. Specifically, you must answer the following questions:

1) Who killed Bart Strunk?

2) Who killed Wayne Metzger?

3) How was Metzger killed? You must be specific as to how the crime was perpetrated.

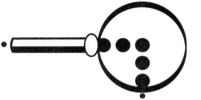

INSPECTOR FORSOOTH ANSWERS YOUR QUESTIONS

Q1—Did Metzger collapse because he ate something containing peanut oil?

That's right. It was determined that Metzger died from an allergic reaction that closed his larynx, and traces of peanut oil were found in this stomach.

Q2—Was Metzger poisoned by something in his lunch?

The answer, literally speaking, is no. But he was poisoned, all right. (Note that peanut oil isn't a poison as such, but it is considered a poison in this case, given Metzger's allergy.)

Q3—Did the bottled water or cups play an important role?

The answer is an emphatic yes. The existence of the cups was an essential part of the conspiracy, believe it or not.

Q4—From what distance was Strunk shot?

It simply wouldn't have been possible for anyone to have shot Strunk from afar, because the shots came from an almost head-on angle, eliminating the possibility that the killer had been farther down along the shore. And because of the dense woods, the shots would never have gotten through unless the killer was near the shore.

Q5—Does that mean that someone in the group closest to the pier must have fired the shot?

Absolutely. Remember, though, those groups rotated.

Q6—Which group was scheduled to have been closest to the pier after the lunch break?

Kevin Van Allen's.

Q7—Was it a coincidence that Sharon Sturgis attended to Wayne Metzger?

Not at all. The entire murder plot depended on who took care of which corpse!

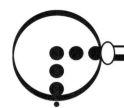

Q8—How long does an allergy to peanut oil take to set in?
Not very long. Metzger probably didn't last more than 15 seconds or so.

Q9—Was it the candied apple that was laced with peanut oil? And did someone know that Metzger was going to eat Strunk's apple?
Believe it or not, the answer to both questions is a resounding yes!

Q10—Was one of the dead guys involved in the conspiracy?
Again, yes!

Q11—Did Willoughby have an alibi?
His alibi was that the apple was still white. Given that he was in a remote locale just prior to when the body was found, it appeared that he couldn't have been involved, because an apple core will turn brown fairly quickly if left out in the open.

Q12—Who died first, Strunk or Metzger?
Great question. The answer is that Strunk died first.

Can you solve the mystery?

Solution on page 180

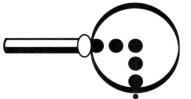

SOLUTIONS

SOLUTION TO "MURDER AROUND THE CLOCK" (page 95)

1) Who killed Bruce Berringer?
The killer was Sean McGillicuddy, the milkman.
2) How can the other suspects be ruled out?
There are two ways to solve the murder—the hard way and the easy way. First off, we note that when Berringer wrote "1:30 hence," he wasn't referring to the time of the shooting; he was referring to what the position of the clocks would be 1 hour and 30 minutes hence. (As discussed in the Q&A, the "hence" meant "in the future," not "therefore.")

The hard way to solve the crime is to use a semaphore code directly. At approximately 2:37 Mountain Time (the time zone in Bogusville), it would be 3:37 in Chicago, the first of the seven clocks on the wall. But if you look at the hand positions at 3:37, you'll see they are quite close to the flag positions of the letter "M" in the semaphore alphabet (right arm at a slight angle to the left, left arm almost straight out to the right).

Now apply the same logic to each of the seven clocks. At 2:37 Mountain Time, it would be 10:37 in Paris, which corresponds roughly with the "I" in semaphore. And so on for Los Angeles ("L"=1:37), Cairo ("K"=11:37), Mexico City ("M"=3:37), Caracas ("A"=5:37), and New York ("N"=4:37). The correspondences aren't all perfect (Berringer was a dying man, after all), but there is a strong match between the indicated times and letters. Together, the letters spell out "MILKMAN." Berringer was identifying Sean McGillicuddy, the milkman, as his killer.

But you didn't need to know semaphore to figure this case out. The "easy" way is to observe that Chicago and Mexico City are in the same time zone, meaning that they would signify the same letter in the semaphore alphabet! Right away we know that Berringer couldn't have been referring to Dowling or Walters (the only two suspects whose last names have seven letters), because neither name has any repeated letters. The only conclusion is that Berringer, true to his approach to life,

must have been identifying his killer by using the man's profession, not his name.

Wouldn't you know that each of the five professions—CATERER, PLUMBER, MILKMAN, REFEREE, and MAÎTRE D'—has seven letters? However, we can rule out four of them as follows:

Using the same logic as we used earlier for the names Dowling and Walters, the killer couldn't have been the plumber or the maître d', because each letter in those job titles is distinct. Similarly, the position of the clocks couldn't possibly be identifying the referee (four e's), or the caterer (two sets of repeated letters). "MILKMAN" was the only job that had one and only one repeated letter, spelling doom for Sean McGillicuddy.

McGillicuddy thought he had stumbled onto the perfect alibi when first questioned concerning his whereabouts at 1:30 a.m., a time when he in fact was out with several others who could vouch for him. But at Interactive Mysteries, we always get our man.

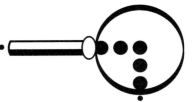

SOLUTION TO "WARM-BLOODED MURDER" (page 101)

1) Who killed Vince Fernald and why?

Clancy McTigue is the guilty party. Here's what happened:

Sometime during the night prior to the primary, McTigue broke into the town hall in order to rig one of the voting machines in favor of his candidate, Michael Doucette. (Note that "Doucette" is next to "Dole" alphabetically. What McTigue did was to insert a paper strip that reversed the two candidates' names, confident that no one would notice the reversal.) Fernald, ready for bed and dressed in pajamas (in case you were wondering about the "scantily clad" part), looked outside from his nearby home and saw that something was amiss. He threw on his overcoat and went to check things out. That's when he came across McTigue, who killed him in the heat of the moment. McTigue then deposited the overcoat miles away in an unsuccessful attempt to get investigators looking in the wrong place.

2) How could the other suspects be ruled out?

The important point is that the murder occurred sometime very early Tuesday morning or even Monday night, as opposed to during the day on Tuesday, when McTigue had an alibi. How do we know this? Well, Clem Woolsey would ordinarily have removed the trash during the day on Tuesday, but his schedule had been altered because of the President's Day holiday on Monday. Had his schedule been normal, it would have proved that the murder occurred after the trash pickup, but this was not the case. When Woolsey went to the town hall dumpster, he was simply checking out the trash to find out what was in store for him the following day! (The shift of one day also explains why he was seen in an area that appeared to be in violation of his schedule.)

Clem is of course a very unlikely suspect, because if he had shoved Fernald into the dumpster, he surely would have been silent about it, preferring to dump the body off the next morning. He might even have made a special trip to the town hall, the Monday holiday notwithstanding. Either way, he certainly wouldn't have called attention to his own misdeed!

As for Luc Evans-Wood, note that his remarks about the temperature seemed to support McTigue's innocence, because had it actually been five degrees Fahrenheit outside, the pool of blood would almost

certainly have frozen had the body been there for any length of time. However, Evans-Wood is Canadian and therefore would use the Celsius scale! Five degrees Celsius is 41 degrees Fahrenheit, well above the freezing level. We know that Evans-Wood is Canadian because he drove "down" to Jasper Falls—which, although fictitious, is located near Dixville Notch, in northernmost New Hampshire. Also, Evans-Wood received mail the previous day, which he couldn't have done had he been in the United States, because the U.S. Postal Service is closed on President's Day. Most important of all, the fact that he is Canadian substantiates his claim that he had no particular interest in the outcome of the election. He certainly had no motive to be involved in either vote tampering or the murder of Vince Fernald. (How's that for some heavy-duty sleuthing?)

And because Hugh Livingston had been out of town until driving back to post his vote that morning, he has an alibi for the only time that matters. All of which leaves Clancy McTigue. Although McTigue had an alibi throughout the day on Tuesday, the murder had already been committed.

3) How did an examination of the voting records help the investigation?

Although the voting records didn't indicate who voted for whom (the whole purpose of voting machines is to guarantee this privacy), they nonetheless contained some valuable information. First of all, although Vince Fernald was a deeply involved political operative who lived next door to the polling place, an examination of the records would have revealed that he never even voted that day! Had he been alive, he would surely have voted promptly in the morning, but this time around he couldn't, for obvious reasons. This was yet more powerful evidence that the murder had occurred prior to the polls' being open.

In addition, the voting records would have confirmed Clancy McTigue's story—that he hadn't voted until the middle of the afternoon. (Although individual votes aren't recorded, voters' names would be systematically checked off as they reached the polling place.) The reason McTigue waited until the afternoon to vote was that he could go into the rigged booth and remove the phony paper strip after a meaningful block of votes had accumulated. That's why the machine looked normal to the investigators—and that completes the case!

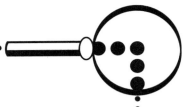

SOLUTION TO "HALLOWEEN HORROR" (page 107)

1) Who killed the ghost?

The murderer was the girl who was trick-or-treating in the cheerleader costume. She planted a poisoned Butterfinger bar in Mrs. MacDonald's candy bowl.

2) How could the killer feel confident that no one other than the intended victim would be killed by the poison?

First of all, the ghost was the next person heading to Mrs. MacDonald's house. Second, even if the ghost elected not to take the Butterfinger bar (which was clearly the best choice available), it was late in the evening, and it was unlikely that another trick-or-treater would come along. Finally, even if the candy bar had not been selected by the ghost or anyone else, Mrs. MacDonald wasn't going to eat it, just as she apparently didn't eat her taffy. You don't see many octogenarians with dentures sinking their (false) teeth into a chewy candy bar.

3) How did the killer's choice of costume play a role?

The cheerleader's costume was complete with a set of pom-poms. (Actually, the correct term is "pompon," but it looks like a typo!) These "pom-poms" came in handy, because they enabled the cheerleader to hide the tainted Butterfinger as she reached into the candy bowl. She then buried the bar so that it wasn't completely obvious, but so that the ghost (with sharper eyes than Mrs. MacDonald) would be able to spot it. And the rest is history.

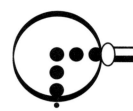

SOLUTION TO "THE PRINTS OF LIGHTNESS" (page 111)

1) Who killed Oscar Delahanty?

The killer was Stan Norton, with an assist (either intentional or otherwise) from Ginger LaCroix.

First of all, Norton killed Oscar Delahanty by smothering him with a pillow. It was apparent that Delahanty must have been alive when the workmen started that morning, because his windows were closed. Ordinarily those windows would have been open at night to give the room some air—as we learned in the question-and-answer session, the house, being a landmark site, would not have been permitted to have central air conditioning. The need for fresh air would have been even greater than usual because of the chemicals used by the floor refinishers. The conclusion is that Delahanty was awakened by the noise of the jackhammer (a necessary part of the hydrant installation, because underground pipes would have to be exposed). He then closed the bedroom window and went back to sleep.

It follows that the killer must have arrived sometime after the workmen started, which was at 8:30 a.m. Therefore, Mitchell Quinn couldn't have been the killer, because he had been in the salon since 8:00.

Ginger LaCroix wasn't the killer, but for a different reason. She was also going to be let go by her boss, and had also harbored thoughts of killing him. Therefore, she started the fire! (Note that she expressed concern about the condition of the house upon hearing that her boss had died of asphyxia; at that point, however, the authorities hadn't mentioned anything about a fire.) Why Norton didn't arrive at the salon until after LaCroix is anyone's guess, but clearly the strangulation occurred before the fire! Note that we don't have a conspiracy between Norton and LaCroix. In fact, their separate confessions suggest they weren't working in cahoots.

2) Who wrongly confessed to the crime?

Ginger LaCroix. She honestly believed that she had killed Delahanty be setting fire to his home. However, Delahanty was already dead by the time Ginger arrived, as suggested by his inability to react to the smoke alarm. Of course, Ginger wasn't completely off the hook. She still faced an arson rap, and was lucky to avoid prosecution for attempted murder!

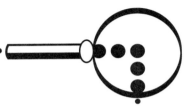

3) How did the coroner's report help identify the killer?

The autopsy would have revealed that Delahanty did not have any soot in his lungs, as would have been expected had he actually died of smoke inhalation. (There would also have been any number of specific indications that he had been smothered, but ruling out smoke inhalation as the cause of death was the most important autopsy finding.)

4) What was the "evidence" that was destroyed?

As Norton left Delahanty's house, he left his footprints on the back steps, which were still not completely dry because of the humid weather. However, this entire area, footprints included, was destroyed in the fire. And that's a wrap.

SOLUTIONS TO "THE FINAL FORECLOSURE" (page 119)

1) Who killed Niles Bronson?

Graham Moss was the killer, assisted by Herman Gertner.

2) What was the role of the accomplice?

To dispose of the murder weapon. After killing Gertner, Moss put the knife in a sheath, placed the sheath in a bag, and dropped it down the trash chute to Gertner, who was waiting on his floor, several floors below, with a basket or some such receptacle to catch it. Gertner later placed the weapon in his bowling bag so he could remove it from the building without attracting suspicion. (Note that Gertner would have been most unlikely to even temporarily survive a plunge of as much as fifteen stories, so one can infer that he lived well below Niles Bronson. Jeff Carrington and Graham Moss, on the other hand, lived above Bronson.)

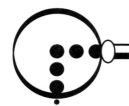

Why not Carrington instead of Moss? Well, note that in his journey through the condominium complex, Inspector Forsooth spoke to the security personnel in between speaking to Moss and Carrington. Why? Because Carrington lived in a penthouse apartment (hence the splendid views), which was accessed via a different elevator bank! To get to Bronson's apartment, Carrington would have had to return to the main floor—as Inspector Forsooth did—where he would have been spotted by the ever-vigilant security folks.

By the way, we know that the building had a trash chute by the fact that Rose was taking her garbage out on a Saturday afternoon (NCAA semi-final games are played on Saturdays). It would be highly unlikely for anyone to come around picking it up on a Saturday or a Sunday, and it would also be unlikely that the garbage would remain in the hallway of such an upscale building.

Note that the description of the murder scene indicates that Bronson was killed before the beginning of the basketball game(s), because his TV was still tuned to FOX ("Tales from the Crypt"), whereas it would have been on CBS had he been alive to watch the basketball. Therefore, neither Moss nor Gertner has any alibi for that time. (I suppose Moss could have changed the channel after killing Bronson to make it look as though he was killed after the games, but Rose Kravitz's intrusion eliminates that possibility.) Finally, the fact that Moss's personal fortunes were turning around is irrelevant. He didn't find out about the accounting firm moving into his building until Monday, by which time Bronson was already dead.

3) Who killed Herman Gertner and why?

Either Gertner was trying to blackmail Moss or expose him. Either way, Gertner wasn't cooperating, and Moss decided to get rid of him, too. Case closed.

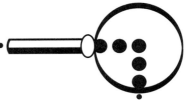

SOLUTION TO "A TRAIL OF TWO CITIES" (page 125)

1) Which one of the suspects killed Melba Hoogstratten?
Esther Pogue killed Melba.

2) Indicate why the other suspects couldn't possibly have committed the crime. Be complete!

As indicated during the question-and-answer session, the alibis depended on where the murder took place. With that in mind, let's look at the alibis for Clyde Finch and Monte Trowbridge.

In Finch's case, if the murder had taken place in the U.S., the "solicitor" alibi would apply to him, because that's the term for a door-to-door salesman. But if the murder took place in the U.K., Finch would have already died! That's because, by assumption, he had only five months to live, whereas Foxy, the German shepherd, would have been quarantined for six months before being allowed to live in the U.K.—that's standard procedure to guard against a rabies outbreak, and explains why Question #12 came into the picture. Either way, Finch could not have committed the crime.

Now consider Monte Trowbridge. He could not have committed the crime in the U.S., because the gas station attendant noted that his right front bumper (where Melba would have been struck, had the hit-and-run occurred on the right side of the road) was devoid of any markings. However, had Melba been murdered in the U.K., the "solicitor" alibi would have applied to him. Either way, Monte is innocent.

Although sleuths weren't required to say anything about Esther Pogue's would-be alibi, it was clear that the whole story about the dog didn't hold water. Evidently Pogue had her car repainted, but there is no guarantee that Foxy would have recognized it in the first place—and, in any event, the repainted car would have looked different, assuming that the shift was, say, from blue to red. (Dogs are, in fact, color blind with respect to some color combinations.)

That's it!

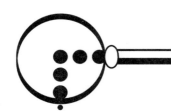

SOLUTION TO "TIMING IS EVERYTHING" (page 131)

1) Who killed James Hooligan?
Muriel Huxley.

2) Explain the key elements of timing in this case.

First of all, the bathroom light of Hooligan's case simply burned out; it bore no relationship to the crime! (Before you cry "foul play," let me say that this little nugget came from a real case. Unlikely, but true.)

As for the method, Muriel had cut the combination lock off a couple of days before the murder, and had replaced it with an identical-looking combination lock. Her husband never realized the change had taken place, because he didn't have any occasion to get into the toolshed in the meantime. Muriel also took the rifle out at that earlier time. She killed Hooligan prior to the meeting between her husband, Martinez, and Plotz, and she ditched the rifle in the woods, just as she had ditched the bolt cutters a couple of days before. But the extra rust on the bolt cutters suggested they might have been outside longer than just one night. A fatal mistake.

A couple of other small "timing" clues point Muriel's way. Remember that when she came down with the news of Hooligan's death, she had just finished planting all those daffodil bulbs. But she couldn't have been planting all that long; it was still morning, and besides, she had just heard the radio announcement, which presumably had been mentioned many times on her all-news station. It follows that she had been doing her gardening for several days despite her being "locked out" of the shed, taking advantage of her husband's preoccupation with the kickback scheme.

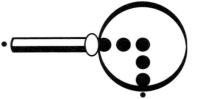

3) What was the missing piece of evidence that tied the murderer to the crime?

The missing piece of evidence was the other lock—the one Muriel Huxley bought to replace the lock she cut off with the bolt cutters! (If you guessed the burned-out lightbulb in Hooligan's bathroom, take credit for some good sleuthing.)

And just why did Muriel kill James Hooligan? Because she and her husband were getting along dreadfully, and she saw a way out of the marriage, the blackmailing, everything. She knew that her husband and/or his henchmen would be blamed for the crime, precisely because she had no apparent motive. Unfortunately for poor Muriel, she was now going to a place where someone else would hold the key to the lock.

SOLUTION TO "THE PIANO REQUITAL" (page 137)

1) Who killed Gilbert von Stade?

Vivien Frechette. She felt she was every bit von Stade's equal (as evidenced by her strong performance of the complicated piece he had chosen), but she never got anywhere near the recognition he did. That's right: Gilbert von Stade was the victim of professional jealousy.

2) What was the method, and why did it work?

Just before the beginning of the show, Frechette laced a couple of black keys in the upper (right-hand) region of the piano with a combination of batrachotoxin and DMSO (dimethyl sulfoxide, in case you want to impress your friends). Note that she didn't have to go to South America to find the poison; it is available at various medical labs in the United States, for example. And all it took was a few drops.

As discussed in the question-and-answer session, DMSO plays a vital role because of its property of being quickly absorbed into the body. DMSO is capable of carrying other compounds into the bloodstream along with it, even if the person's only contact with the mixture is with the surface of the skin. However, one of DMSO's common side effects is that it leaves the user with a garlicky taste in his mouth! (Note:

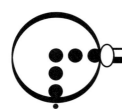

It was quite unlikely that von Stade's garlic breath came from something he ate. After all, he was in the men's room between the dinner and the performance, and he could have used any of the items there to deal with the garlic taste that he plainly disliked.)

The reason why Heinrich Albertson wasn't killed is that his piece (Etude in C major) uses almost no black keys, whereas von Stade's piece (Etude in G flat) is commonly referred to as Chopin's "black-key" étude, such is its emphasis on flats and sharps. Because the poisonous solution was a skimmed-on liquid, von Stade might have noticed that something was amiss, but, being the seasoned professional that he was, he evidently concluded that the show must go on.

In theory, the fact that the show went on would have boded poorly for Vivien Frechette, who followed von Stade in the evening's program. But von Stade had basically wiped the keys clean with his hands; in addition, Frechette's first piece, being slow and melancholy, was much longer than the others, which, coupled with the disruption following von Stade's death, would have given the remaining solution time to evaporate under the stage lights! These factors all but eliminated the possibility that a lethal or even toxic dosage could have made its way into her bloodstream. (Also, her first piece uses almost exclusively the white keys in the lower ranges of the keyboard, as opposed to the higher-pitched flats and sharps of the black-key étude.)

Theoretically, it was possible that someone who wasn't familiar with the music was trying to kill Heinrich Albertson instead, but the only person who was unfamiliar with sheet music was Marla Albertson; however, she was still very much in love with her husband, and had no apparent reason to do him in. And that's a wrap.

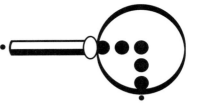

SOLUTION TO "THE VALENTINE'S DAY MASSACRE" (page 143)

1) Who killed Rudy Marcus?

Daphne Nagelson killed Rudy Marcus.

2) Rudy's personality played a role in his demise, in two distinct ways. Name them.

First, and most obviously, Rudy's philandering is what got him in trouble. Second, Rudy was a victim of the accountant in him. When he bought Mary Stahl a gold necklace in California, he had it shipped home, thereby avoiding the state sales tax. Unfortunately for Rudy, when his business trip was delayed, the UPS delivery person arrived with his package before he was home to receive it. The delivery person left either the package or a little slip of paper (we don't really know which) in Rudy's vestibule. Whatever was left bore the markings of a California boutique, which didn't go unnoticed by Daphne when she stopped by to drop off her present to Rudy. At the time, she doubtless thought the present was for her, hence the smile on her face. When she got the emerald brooch instead, she may have been delighted to receive it, but she immediately knew that Rudy was a two-timer. (The fact that Rudy's trip was delayed also explains why Cornelia did not hear Mary Stahl's message. Because Rudy never called Cornelia while he was gone to tell her of his changed plans, she ended her housesitting on the 12th, not the 13th.)

3) The testimony of two particular people would prove very helpful in bringing the guilty party to justice. Which two people?

The people who would prove helpful in bringing the guilty party to justice are Mrs. Wheelock, who could confirm that Daphne had visited Rudy's home the day before the murder, and the delivery person, who could confirm that the slip of paper (or package) had been left prior to Daphne's arrival. The combination of these two testimonies would have been important in establishing Daphne's guilt.

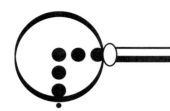

SOLUTION TO "WHERE THERE'S A WILL" (page 149)

1) Who killed Marion Webster?
The killer was Gwen.

2) Where was the murder weapon hidden after the crime?
Before the murder, Gwen had hollowed out one of the thick reference books in her father's study. That's where she placed the murder weapon immediately following the killing. It didn't occur to the bungling first team of investigators to look within the study itself. (You did better, I'm sure. It's an old trick.) At some point she had a chance to go in and replace the hollow book with a real one.

3) Which of the children was Webster going to treat harshly in his revised will? (One of them is the killer!)
Marion Webster had decided to change his will to give Gwen a fake necklace ("put on ice") instead of the family heirloom. That was her motive. The others to be treated harshly by their father were Herbert (who had a fine "past as a lad," but who had disappointed his father thereafter) and Dorothy (whose library donations were going to be reduced).

Note that of the three losers in Webster's to-be-revised will, only Gwen's whereabouts were not accounted for. She alone had motive and opportunity.

The "winners" included Eugene (Gene), as tipped off by Webster saying that "Gene rates income"—meaning that he should receive the bond portfolio. The other two winners were Biff and Laura, who benefited from their father's saying that "funding for 'libraries' would increase." Laura (late September) was a Libra and Biff (April 1) was an Aries. The "signs getting crossed" was a reference to the fact that the word "libraries" forces the two signs of the zodiac to share the letter "a." And that's a wrap!

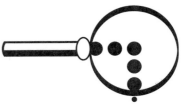

SOLUTION TO "THE OVERHEAD SMASH" (page 153)

1) Who killed Manny Heitz? What was the murder scenario?

Roger Dant killed Manny Heitz. Dant arrived at Heitz's residence before the 11:00 match and the two got into an argument. The result was that Dant knocked Heitz out and took his place as a linesman. (With sunglasses and a visor, the disguise was made easier. The only people who would have known the difference were too far away. Note also that Dant and Heitz were about the same size.) Heitz was left bound and gagged until after the match. When Dant returned, the two got into another struggle, one that resulted in Heitz's death.

The reason the two got into an argument in the first place was that Dant wanted Chris de la Harpe to win the tennis match. Heitz wasn't willing to be bribed, so Dant decided to take matters into his own hands—making bad calls in de la Harpe's favor to facilitate the upset.

2) What was the crucial piece of evidence that the killer tried to cover up? Why was his effort doomed to failure?

The crucial piece of evidence against Dant was that his sneakers had clay on them from the stadium court at Forest Hills. The year was 1975, and the U.S. Open was being played on clay for the first time. That year, the early men's matches were two out of three sets, not three out of five, which is why the Molotov/de la Harpe match was so short, which in turn enabled Dant to be there for the whole match and still make it to Heitz's house and then the public courts by 1:00 p.m. Also, this explains my "highly misleading" answer to Question #4, in which I note that Heitz lived 15 minutes away from the National Tennis Center at Flushing Meadows (where the U.S. Open moved in 1978). Had I wanted to be more helpful, I would have added that he lived right next to the stadium at Forest Hills! (By the way, the "political intrigue" of that particular U.S. Open was the fact that Martina Navratilova announced her defection to the United States!)

Dant realized that after he killed Heitz, he was in big trouble. He therefore scampered to the local public courts, which were also clay (technically Har-Tru, a green, granular, clay-like surface). By picking up a game, Dant found someone who could vouch for his whereabouts. He also made sure someone noticed his vanity plate. (As noted during the question-and-answer session, New York license plates were orange

before the bicentennial year of 1976, when they went to a more conventional red and blue lettering on a white background.) Most important of all, Dant was able to get Har-Tru granules on his sneakers, covering up the fact that he had been on the stadium court.

What Dant hadn't counted on was that Manny Heitz was wearing brand-new sneakers! The absence of Har-Tru granules on the soles of Heitz's sneakers proved he hadn't been at the 11:00 match after all.

3) Name one person whom the prosecution would surely want as a witness for their side.

One person who could have served as a witness for the prosecution was Tracy Molotov. He got a close look at Dant, and despite the visor and sunglasses, he would have been unlikely to forget his face!

SOLUTION TO "PIER FOR THE COURSE" (page 159)

1) Who killed Bart Strunk?
David Willoughby.
2) Who killed Wayne Metzger?
Again, David Willoughby.
3) How was Metzger killed? You must be specific as to how the crime was perpetrated.

The conspiracy was between senior vice president Wayne Metzger and vice president David Willoughby. Metzger pressured Willoughby into shooting Bart Strunk so that he (Metzger) could take over the reins of the company.

But Willoughby insisted on having an alibi. He agreed to shoot Strunk just as he was finishing his caramel apple. The plan was that Metzger would then place the apple core in a cup of water—this would prevent the apple from "aging," as it would if left in the air, and would make it seem as though Strunk had been shot at a time when Willoughby wasn't in the area. Metzger agreed, the idea being that Willoughby would leave the pier area for a remote site, at which point Metzger would wait a little while before getting help, then would take the apple out of the water to disguise the time of the killing and provide Willoughby with an alibi.

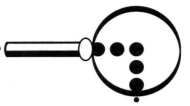

The only wrinkle was that Willoughby, standing at a point on the shore, killed Strunk a bit too soon—on purpose! Metzger found that the apple was too big to fit in the cup of water, and he therefore hurriedly ate the rest of it himself! This is precisely what Willoughby had anticipated. He knew he had a chance to kill two birds with one stone (ultimately he felt angry at being Metzger's flunky for so many years), and he had taken the opportunity to place peanut oil on the outside of Strunk's caramel apple at its widest point—when, ostensibly, he was checking Metzger's food to make sure he had a ham sandwich instead of peanut butter and jelly. The taste of the peanut oil was obscured by the caramel, and of course Strunk consumed it without any side effects. But Metzger's intense allergy to peanut oil (a well-known and very serious condition) caused his larynx to tighten up within mere seconds of its ingestion. Metzger had time to place the apple in the water cup, but that's about it. He never made it off the pier.

The final touch was that Willoughby made sure he found the bodies first, confident that the others would be distracted by their own projects. When he arrived with Sharon Sturgis, he saw to it that she attended to Wayne Metzger, so that he could attend to Strunk. Willoughby simply removed the apple from the cup of water, thereby creating the illusion that his alibi depended on.

That's it!

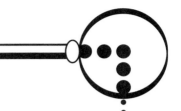

FIVE-MINUTE CRIMEBUSTERS
CLEVER MINI-MYSTERIES

STAN SMITH

ILLUSTRATED BY
KATHLEEN O'MALLEY

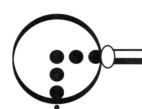

INTRODUCTION

WELCOME BACK, sleuths and solvers, to the puzzling world of amateur logician Thomas P. Stanwick! From his home in the small town of Baskerville and in his travels in New England and the British Isles, Stanwick uses his amazing powers of deduction to help the police and others solve many a baffling crime. He also helps friends and neighbors in Baskerville solve less felonious, but equally puzzling, mysteries of their own.

Stanwick helps Inspector Matt Walker of the Royston Police, Inspector Gilbert Bodwin of Scotland Yard, and attorney Amanda Tucker solve murders in Royston, London, and elsewhere. Sometimes Stanwick visits the scene, but at other times he deduces the solution from the comfort of an armchair. His cases include robbery, fraud, espionage, and general high jinks at home and abroad. And sometimes Stanwick helps a friend or a neighbor logically untie a puzzling problem.

These cases require Thomas Stanwick to deduce essential facts from physical circumstances, separate liars from truthtellers, infer who has what role in a gang or crime, and reason, with elementary mathematics or time sequences. So get ready to test and sharpen your logical thinking skills and help Stanwick unravel these mystery puzzles!

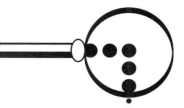

THE STOCKBROKER'S LAST MORNING

SHORTLY AFTER NINE one morning, Inspector Walker's car pulled up in front of a large office building in downtown Royston. With Walker was Thomas P. Stanwick, the amateur logician. Stanwick had been visiting Walker at headquarters when the call reporting the sudden death of Charles Steinberg came in.

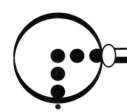

Stanwick and Walker hurried to Steinberg's seventh-floor office suite, from which he had run a prosperous stock brokerage. Passing through the carpeted reception area, they entered Steinberg's spacious office.

Steinberg's body was slumped in an easy chair near a small, circular table in the center of the room. His tie and collar were loose. He had been dead for less than an hour, and showed no sign of bleeding. On a small table by the wall, a typewriter contained a typed note, which Stanwick read aloud.

"I see no further purpose to my life and have therefore decided to end it. I hope my family, friends, and associates will not blame themselves. Goodbye."

Walker turned to the man in his early 30s who was standing near the office door. Jon Golding was a vice president of the firm.

"What can you tell us, Mr. Golding?"

Golding coughed nervously.

"I entered Mr. Steinberg's office earlier this morning to see him on urgent business. He was sitting in the easy chair with a cup of coffee in his hand. As soon as he saw me, he hastily drank it down. The cup had no sooner left his lips than he was seized with terrible convulsions. A few seconds later he was dead. I was horrified and ran out to the receptionist's desk, where I phoned for help. No one was allowed into the office until you arrived."

"Did you see the note in the typewriter?"

"No, sir, I did not."

"Thank you." Walker went over to Steinberg's body and searched his pockets. In the right jacket pocket he found a small glass vial, which he sniffed. "This probably contained the poison."

Stanwick sniffed it and, taking out his handkerchief, picked up the emptied coffee cup from its saucer on the table and sniffed it also.

"I can detect a whiff of it here, too," he said.

Stanwick put down the coffee cup and faced Golding.

"Mr. Golding," he asked, "did Mr. Steinberg usually have his coffee in that chair?"

"Yes, sir, he drank his coffee and read the paper in that chair every morning about this time."

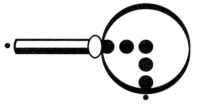

Stanwick pointed to a newspaper folded neatly on the table. "Did you put that there?"

Golding flushed slightly. "It was there when I came in. He wasn't reading it."

Stanwick abruptly left the office and walked to the desk of the young receptionist.

"What can you tell us, Miss Gwynne?"

"Why, little enough, I'm afraid. I heard some typing in Mr. Steinberg's office, and then Mr. Golding came out of his own office to pick up some documents for Mr. Steinberg. He went into Mr. Steinberg's office and a few moments later came rushing wildly out here and phoned for help."

"What documents did he want to show Mr. Steinberg?"

"Why, some draft pages of our weekly newsletter. He dropped them on the floor as he came back out."

Reentering Steinberg's office, Stanwick put another question to Golding. "I see there is a door between your office and his. Why didn't you use that when you came in to see him?"

"Miss Gwynne, our receptionist, had the newsletter pages I wanted to show him," Golding answered.

Stanwick quietly drew Walker aside.

"Golding is lying, Matt," he said. "This isn't suicide, but murder!"

How does Stanwick know Golding is lying?

Solution on page 248

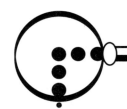

A MODEL MURDER

Curiosity and sadness mingled in the mind of Thomas P. Stanwick, amateur logician, as he parked his car near the home of Lola Monteray in Royston. His friend Inspector Matt Walker had called to tell him of the murder of the beautiful young model and had invited him to have a look at the scene. Not even the intellectual satisfaction of studying crimes could blot out for Stanwick the tragedy of untimely death.

He entered the trim, white Monteray home and was shown upstairs. Walker was in the bedroom. The body of Lola Monteray, in a lacy nightgown, lay prone on the blood-soaked bed sheets. A large, blood-covered knife lay beside the bed.

"The coroner estimates that Lola Monteray was stabbed to death around two o'clock this morning," said Walker briskly. "No prints in here except for hers. She was discovered this morning by Thomas Larch, her agent, who says he stopped by to take her to an important meeting with some designers. He found the back door unlocked and searched the house until he found her here."

Stanwick glanced around the plainly furnished room and toyed with the tip of his mustache.

"Have you found a possible motive?" he asked.

Walker shook his head.

"Not yet. She seems to have been successful and well liked. Her appointment book shows that she had lunch with her boyfriend, Scott Phillips, two days ago. I called him and told him she had been found dead at her home. He said he'd come right over. When he arrives, he might be able to tell us if anything unusual was going on in her life."

The two men left the room and went downstairs. A pudgy man with a dark Lincoln beard sat in the living room, looking crushed with grief.

"Mr. Larch, I presume," said Stanwick with a nod as he strode in. "I understand that you found the body."

"Yes," the agent replied, his head bowed. "An awful sight!"

"Why were you so persistent as to enter and search the house to find her?"

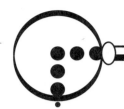

Larch looked up wearily. "We had a 10:30 appointment at the Picardio Studio," he said. "This was an important meeting that might have led to a lucrative contract, and she knew it. I wasn't going to lose a deal like that so that she could sleep late!"

At that moment the front door was flung open with a crash, and a disheveled young man ran up the stairs.

"Who stabbed my sweetheart?" he shouted. "Let me see her!"

A policeman stopped him at the top of the stairs and brought him forcibly down to the living room.

"Mr. Phillips?" said Walker. "I'm very sorry. The crime scene is accessible only to investigators. Miss Monteray was killed about two this morning and was discovered a little later. Her appointment book shows that you two had lunch together on Tuesday. Did she give any indication that someone was threatening her?"

Phillips thrust his hands into his pockets and paced the rug.

"No, nothing. She was excited about an appointment to visit Picardio's this morning, and talked about the work she hoped to do for them. She was very happy."

Stanwick, ensconced in an armchair, watched idly as Phillips paced.

"Where did you eat?" he asked.

"Marygold's, downtown," answered Phillips. "She loved their asparagus tips."

"The best in town." Stanwick arose languidly and stretched. "Well, Matt, earn your pay. It's time to arrest the killer!"

Who murdered Lola Monteray?

Solution on page 248

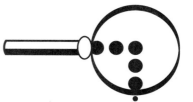

THE ADVENTURE OF THE NEGATIVE CLUE

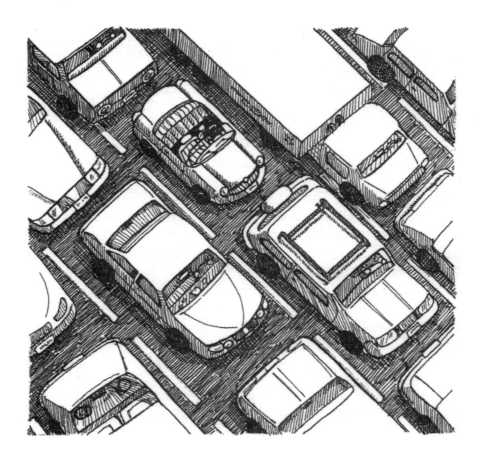

NOT EVEN THE UNUSUAL HEAT of that late spring day could dissuade Thomas P. Stanwick from driving into the city. The amateur logician had learned that one of Royston's most select book dealers was holding a sale of rare folios at two in the afternoon. His bibliophilic instincts aroused, Stanwick was braving the heat and the downtown traffic he detested when the police radio in his car reported a murder

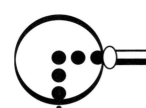

nearby.

A middle-aged man had been stabbed to death in Hardee's Hardware Store three blocks away. Squad cars were told to watch for a white male of five feet, ten inches, 160 pounds, about 22 years old, with black hair and a pencil mustache, wearing a white T-shirt, a leather jacket, and blue jeans.

Stanwick wrestled with his competing interests for two seconds and then turned toward the hardware store. Parking his car down the block, he walked through a curious throng and, with a flash of his police pass, entered the shop. Inspector Walker arched his sandy eyebrows in surprise as he caught sight of his friend.

"Hello, Matt," said Stanwick. "I heard the bulletin on the radio and thought I'd stop by for a look."

"Glad to see you, Tom." Walker nodded to a dead body crumpled on the floor in front of the sales counter. "There's what there is to look at."

The victim was a dark-haired man in his middle 40s. He lay face-up. The handle of a knife protruded from his ribs, and a circle of blood had soaked through his blue suit.

"His wallet is missing," Walker reported dryly, "as is a briefcase the sales clerk said he was carrying when he came in. From other papers in his pockets, we've identified him as Hubert French, an accounting executive from Helston."

"Did the clerk see it happen?" asked Stanwick, glancing at a thin, balding man lurking behind the counter.

"No. He says French came in to pick up a special wrench he had ordered. A guy fitting the bulletin description came in just a few seconds later. The clerk went to the back to get the wrench. While there, he heard sounds of a scuffle and a cry from here. He rushed in and found French dead and the other fellow gone."

Stanwick fingered the tip of his mustache. "Any prints on the weapon?"

Walker shook his head. "No. The clerk says our suspect wore gloves."

Just then the outer door opened, and two policemen entered with a manacled man closely fitting the description given on the radio.

"Inspector, this is T. A. Orrison," said the older officer. "We found

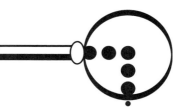

him four blocks away, walking briskly down Jefferson. Says he was on his way home after slicing fish in the back of Radford's Fish Mart all morning. He fits the description, though, so we picked him up."

Walker looked coldly at Orrison, who was wearing green sunglasses.

"What do you know about this, Mr. Orrison?" he demanded, pointing at the corpse.

"Nothing," Orrison replied angrily. "I was at work all morning. I haven't been in this place for at least three weeks."

"How long have you worked at Radford's?"

"Two months now, part-time. I work from seven to noon, six days a week. I put in some overtime today and was just on the way home when I was grabbed by these two guys in a squad car and brought

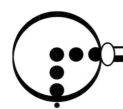

here."

A mild, metallic odor suffused the small shop. Stanwick wandered to a window, opened it partway, and gazed idly out. Walker continued his questions.

"You implied that you visited this shop a few weeks ago. Why?"

"I dunno. I had to get nails or tape or something."

"Why did you work late today?"

"We got a big catch in this morning, and I was the only one there."

Walker signaled to the uniformed officers. "All right, that's enough for now. Take him to the station for more questioning."

Once the others had left, Stanwick rejoined the inspector.

"When you get back, Matt," he said, "you may as well book him for the murder. He's your man."

Walker turned to him in astonishment. "What makes you so sure? I'll admit he's on shaky ground, but I don't see any conclusive clue."

Stanwick smiled.

"In a way, there isn't one," he replied. "What's really significant in this case is what you could call a negative clue—the one that isn't here!"

What is the negative clue?

Solution on page 248

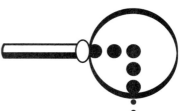

THE CASE OF
THE INVISIBLE MURDERER

THOMAS P. STANWICK, the amateur logician, and Inspector Matthew Walker of the Royston Police Department were grateful for the sea breeze on that hot August day as they walked from Walker's car to the entryway of the Sea Maiden restaurant. The two had been discussing another case in Walker's office when the call had come in about a murder at the Sea Maiden.

Inside the stuffy restaurant, two uniformed officers were recording the names and addresses of those who had been there when the body was discovered. The discovery had occurred at 3:30, less than an hour before Stanwick and Walker arrived, so only six patrons—one couple and a family of four—were being detained. They sat in a row of chairs along a side wall. With them were a cashier, a busboy, two waiters, two waitresses, and the chef.

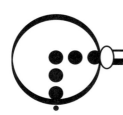

Walker introduced himself to the agitated owner of the restaurant, Steven Evans. Evans, Walker, and Stanwick then passed through the main dining room, which contained 17 tables, to a smaller dining room on the right.

"Hello, Ernie," said Walker to the police photographer. "Are you fellows about through?"

"Just about. Jim is still dusting for prints."

The smaller room was connected to the main room by an open doorway. One of the five tables still had dirty utensils and dishes of half-eaten food. Slumped across this table was the dead man, a wealthy publishing executive named Gerald Hottleman. A knife protruded from his back.

"It was a restaurant steak knife with no prints," reported the fingerprinter. "Wiped clean." Walker nodded and glanced around the plainly decorated room. Several small windows near the ceiling did little to relieve the warmth and stuffiness of the room. An odor of fish lingered in the air.

"How was the body discovered?" Walker asked Evans.

"About an hour ago, Kris, the waitress for this room, started to come in to ask Mr. Hottleman if he wanted coffee or dessert," replied the perspiring owner. "She saw him from the doorway and stood there, screaming."

196

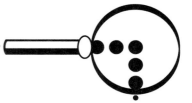

"No one else was in this room, then?" asked Stanwick.

"He was the only one in here. An elderly couple who had lunch here left about 20 minutes before we found Mr. Hottleman."

"Did anyone see Hottleman alive after they left?" Walker inquired.

"Oh, yes. When the old folks were about halfway to the cash register, Mr. Hottleman came out and gave the lady her sunglasses, which she had left on the table."

"Then Hottleman came back here?"

"That's right."

"And who else entered the room between the time Hottleman returned to his table and the time his body was discovered?"

"Why, no one, Inspector. The other guests were in the main dining room, and Kris was on break."

Stanwick eyed the owner quizzically. "How can you be sure that no one slipped into this room?" he asked.

"I was sitting at a small table near the cash register looking over our receipts," Evans replied, "and I would have noticed it."

Just then the medical examiner's staff entered the room to remove the body. Evans excused himself and hurried off. Walker returned to the main room to talk to the uniformed officers. Stanwick lingered in the small room and glanced about, thoughtfully fingering a tip of his mustache.

No doorways led into the room except the one from the main dining room. The windows were too small for human entry and too high up for the knife to have been thrown in from outside, even if the angle of the knife in the body permitted such a hypothesis. Stanwick frowned, returned to the main room, and took Walker aside.

"Matt, was anything taken?" he asked quietly.

"Hottleman's wallet is gone. If you mean evidence, nothing was touched until we arrived."

"Then how was Hottleman identified?"

"The owner and staff here know him. He's been here many times."

"Rather late for lunch, isn't it?" Stanwick smiled slightly.

Walker shrugged. "Not everyone thought so."

The two walked back to the side room and paused by the doorway. Photographers, fingerprinters, and medical examiners were gone, as were the dead man and the murder weapon. The busboy apologeti-

cally brushed by Stanwick and Walker with a small cart and began to clear the effects of the victim's table.

"We're still taking statements," said Walker quietly, "but everything we've heard so far corroborates the owner's story. He was seated at the table near the cash register the whole time. Frankly, Tom, I'm puzzled. The only way anyone could enter the room is through this doorway. No one was in there after the old couple left except for Hottleman; he was seen reentering the room; and no one else was seen entering the room until the body was discovered."

"An impossible crime, eh?" chuckled Stanwick. "Or at least a crime committed by an invisible killer. Well, there are more ways than one to be invisible, my friend. I can tell you who the murderer is."

Who murdered Hottleman?

Solution on page 249

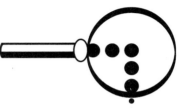

DEATH BRINGS DOWN THE CURTAIN

TWO SHOTS CRACKED from the barrel of the pistol. Morton Hooper, playing the invidious Sam Spearon, crumpled to the stage floor as Lady Carneval (Vanessa Netherwood) and her niece (Elizabeth Murdoch) screamed in horror. The gun still in her hand, Lizzy Belle (Ann Doherty) then fled the stage with her admirer, Ned Hester (Ken Lunch).

The Royston Community Players production of the popular farce "Two Bullets Too Many" was off to a rollicking start. Five minutes after the gunplay, Scene 3 came to an end. Only Netherwood and Murdoch remained on the partly darkened stage during the brief scene change.

Scene 4 opened with a conversation between them. Several minutes into the scene, Lizzy Belle reappeared on stage ranting and waving the pistol. After some wild dialogue, Lizzy took sudden aim and fired two shots at Lady Carneval. This time, however, the fall to the floor and the blood were a little too lifelike, and the screams were genuine.

Thomas P. Stanwick stood up in the audience. "Curtain!"

Some two hours later, the members of the audience had given their names and addresses and had been sent home. The cast and crew were in the greenroom being questioned by the reliable Sergeant Hatch. Stanwick and Inspector Matthew Walker were standing on the otherwise deserted stage, near the bloodstain on the floor.

"It couldn't have been an accident," said Walker. "The props manager, whom I know and trust, has years of experience, and he knows blanks from real bullets. He swears he filled the gun with blanks before the show."

"I think we can rule out suicide, too," Stanwick replied. "Miss Netherwood was on stage the whole time between the shooting of Sam Spearon, which was done with blanks, and the second shooting. She therefore had no chance to change the bullets. She would have had to use an accomplice, and that would have been too risky for both."

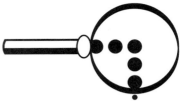

"I agree." Walker sighed. "So murder it was. The first shooting was at 8:40 P.M. Miss Doherty immediately left the stage, dumped the gun in the prop box, and returned to the greenroom to have her makeup touched up. At 8:55 P.M., she picked up the gun again and reappeared on stage. So the bullets must have been switched during that 15-minute interval. And backstage is not accessible to the public."

Just then Sergeant Hatch approached to report to Walker:

"I've finished the preliminary questioning, sir," he said. The stage crew, including the props manager, were in constant communication with one another, and no one had a chance to get to the gun in the prop box during the critical interval. The director was in the audience with some friends.

"Miss Doherty and Mr. Lynch vouch for each other and went to the greenroom between scenes. The makeup artist, who was expecting them, confirms this. Miss Netherwood and Miss Murdoch remained on stage between shootings. Mr. Hooper, the first 'victim,' left the stage at the end of Scene 3, stopped to get a soda from the vending machine, and returned to the greenroom."

"Aren't two other actors in the show?" Walker asked. "Where were they?"

"Lester Sack and Jill Richart were in the greenroom the entire time, waiting to go on in Act II. The best consensus we can get is that Scene 4 opened at 8:47 P.M.; Miss Doherty reappeared with the gun at 8:55 P.M.; and Miss Netherwood was shot at 9:01 P.M."

"Thank you, Hatch. Carry on." Walker returned to Stanwick.

"Apparently some more questioning is in order."

"Indeed," said Stanwick. "Especially with the prime suspect."

Who is Stanwick's prime suspect, and why?

Solution on page 249

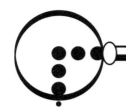

A DEATH BY THE THAMES

"POOR LADY MADGE!" exclaimed Judith Woolbrott. "Sir Alan done to death, her jewels taken, the silver taken—how will she bear it?" The petite maid burst into tears again.

"We have no more questions for now, young lady," said Inspector Gilbert Bodwin of Scotland Yard. "Please remain here."

The inspector and his companion, Thomas P. Stanwick, returned up the stairs to the elegant flat of Sir Alan and Lady Madge Tewksbury. The couple, a prominent industrialist and his wife, lived just across the Thames from Parliament.

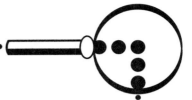

"I'm sorry to take you away from your Churchill Society conference, Tom," said Bodwin, "but I thought this case would interest you. You don't often visit London in November."

"Always glad to be on hand," replied Stanwick as they entered the flat. He and the inspector passed through a small foyer into the living room. An armchair was overturned, and a mahogany case on the sideboard had been torn open and emptied.

"Sir Alan was found lying on the rug in the middle of the room," said Bodwin. "His body has been removed. The examiner's preliminary report is that he was stunned by a blow and then strangled by a pair of large and powerful hands."

Stanwick fingered the tip of his mustache. "The maid, if I recall her answers, reported for duty at 10, found the door unlocked, and then entered the living room and discovered the body. After a fit of screaming, she ran down to the neighbor's flat and has remained there since."

"That's right," said Bodwin. "She clearly is not the murderer, since her hands are much too small and weak. Sir Alan apparently surprised a burglar, who killed him and escaped with some of the family silver—there is the rifled case on the sideboard—and Lady Madge's jewels from her case in the bedroom. Her Ladyship is on her way back from a trip to Scotland."

"How much have she and Miss Woolbrott been told?" asked Stanwick.

"Her Ladyship has been told only the essentials. The maid had to be sedated, and has been told only that her Ladyship is returning."

"Excellent!" Stanwick took his pipe from his pocket, then replaced it with a sheepish grin. "Of course, no smoking at a crime scene. Anyway, I recommend that you question Miss Woolbrott further. She didn't commit the murder herself, but I think she knows who did!"

Why does Stanwick think so?

Solution on page 249

THE TABLE OF DEATH

JUST AS INSPECTOR WALKER'S hand was hovering over a bishop, his beeper alarm sounded. He pushed back his chair with an impatient sigh, and stood up. Across the chessboard, Thomas P. Stanwick chuckled softly.

"Saved by the beep!" he exclaimed.

"Don't be so sure of that!" Walker retorted as he started toward the Royston Chess Club lobby and a telephone. One minute later, he was back.

"Gotta go," he said hurriedly. "Two bodies in an apartment. Want to come?"

"Certainly."

Twenty minutes later, Stanwick and Walker were in a seedy third-floor apartment downtown. The place consisted of a bedroom and a small kitchen off a sparsely furnished sitting room. In the center of the sitting room stood a square wooden table supporting a half-full pitcher of purple liquid, two drained glasses, several incense candles, a few small piles of powder, and a handwritten note with two signatures.

On the floor by the table lay the bodies of two middle-aged men, each by an overturned wooden chair. Sergeant Hatch and the crime scene unit were already at work when Walker and Stanwick arrived.

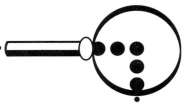

"The fellow in the undershirt is George Barnes, the tenant here," Hatch reported. "The one in the suit is Theo Hunter, an insurance sales- man. We've checked their pockets. The candles and drugs are similar to those used in some cult out West. The note, signed by both, is a suicide pact. It's pretty weird, sir."

"Will that word appear on your report, Sergeant?" said Walker with a wry half-smile. "Let's see what was in their pockets."

"This way, sir." Hatch led them to a side table. "Barnes had these tissues and keys, and this comb and wallet. The rest is Hunter's. Hand- kerchief, keys, penknife, business cards, wallet, comb, a folded gas receipt from earlier today, a folded insurance application from last week."

"Hmmm." Walker turned to the approaching medical examiner. "Any verdict, Doc?"

"Not yet, of course," replied Dr. Pillsbury peevishly. "You must await the autopsy. The external symptoms, though, are of a swift-acting poison."

Walker glanced at Stanwick. "You've been awfully quiet, Tom."

Stanwick, who had been leaning against the wall and staring at the table, snapped out of his reverie.

"It's a small room and a busy investigation," he said. "Just trying to stay out of the way. I suggest that you check the signatures on that note carefully, though."

"Oh?" Walker arched his sandy eyebrows. "That's routine, of course, but why do you say that?"

"I think one of the signatures is forged. This looks to me like a murder-suicide. One poisoned the other and then made it look like a double suicide. And I can tell you which was the murderer."

Which was the murderer? How does Stanwick know?

Solution on page 250

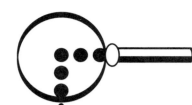

MURDER AT BIG JAKE'S

IT WAS LATE IN the afternoon of a fine spring day when Thomas P. Stanwick, the amateur logician, waved Inspector Matthew Walker into the living room of his Baskerville bungalow. Stanwick, who was recovering from the flu, was dressed in pajamas, slippers, and a dark blue robe. Rufus, his black Labrador, looked up and flopped his tail when the two men entered the room, and then the dog resumed gnawing a plastic bone.

"Glad to hear you're feeling better, Tom," said Walker. He sat down and accepted a can of cold beer.

"I'm getting there, thanks," said Stanwick with a weak smile. He sat down and put his feet on an ottoman. "Haven't had the strength to do much more than read, but I'm behind on the newspapers. What's new in city crime?"

"Well, let's see." Walker took a sip of beer. "A few nights ago, at about two A.M., a drug pusher named Valenzi was shot and killed on the sidewalk in front of Big Jake's bar. A drifter named Albert Gummond was arrested near the scene."

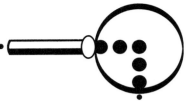

"Although no one saw the actual shooting, witnesses in the bar have identified Gummond as having quarreled with Valenzi there shortly beforehand. Not about drugs, though—about a woman. Gummond left the bar immediately after Valenzi. The gun hasn't been found yet, but Gummond had blood on his jacket when he was picked up. The blood is being tested."

Stanwick lit his pipe. "Has Gummond made a statement?"

"Actually, he made several statements when he was sent over for psychiatric evaluation," Walker replied. "According to the doctor who is checking him, he suffers from a rare psychological disorder, one of occasionally lying compulsively."

"Occasional compulsive lying?"

"Yes." Walker smiled. "In one variation of the disorder, the doc tells me, the patient lies every other statement. In the only other variation, the patient lies every third statement. The doctor can't tell yet which variation Gummond has."

"Extraordinary!" Stanwick's eyes sparkled. "Do you happen to remember what he said?"

"I think I have it here," replied Walker, extracting and flipping open his notebook. "Gummond made five statements: 1) 'I've never been in Big Jake's in my life.' 2) 'I've been in Royston for the last two weeks.' 3) 'I didn't shoot that Valenzi guy.' 4) 'It is not true that I was in Detroit five days ago.' 5) 'I own a gun, but it's with my sister in Chicago.'

"Fascinating," murmured Stanwick distantly. "And where is Gummond now?"

"Still undergoing psych eval," said Walker. "Any thoughts?"

"One or two," Stanwick replied with a yawn. "For one, you can tell the doctor that Gummond suffers from the first variation of the disorder. For another, you can tell the chief that Gummond did the shooting."

How does Stanwick know this?

Solution on page 250

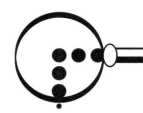

MURDER BY THE WAYWARD

AMANDA TUCKER, attorney at law, smiled and accepted a mug of tea from Thomas P. Stanwick, who then sat down across from her in his usual armchair.

"I'm glad you stopped by, Amanda," the amateur logician said genially. "I haven't seen you in a while. How've you been? And how's Roger?"

"I'm fine, thanks, Tom," she replied. "And so's the boy. He's visiting his father this week; it's spring vacation, you know."

"So it is." Stanwick grinned. "I'm glad I'm not traveling."

"It's just as well he's away. I'm tied up now with a property case I've taken over from Maryellen Beecher. In fact, I'm on my way back from a deposition. Maryellen had to leave the case now that she's representing the prime suspect in the Lubbock murder."

"Lubbock. Wasn't that the fellow shot in the parking lot of the Wayward Inn in East Frailey?" Stanwick asked.

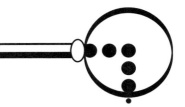

"That's right. Do you know much about it?"

"Not as much as I'd like to."

"Then allow me," said Tucker. "Archie Lubbock, 47, was a trust administrator for a local bank. A widower, he had for two years been dating Maggie Thurston, 35, an aeronautical engineer. Last Monday evening, they met at the inn for dinner. They arrived about 7:30 in separate cars and went in together."

"Partway through the meal, they quarreled. She says she was angry because he was reluctant to visit her parents in Kentucky next summer. Witnesses say she picked up her light jacket and stormed out. He paused just long enough to extract a large bill from his wallet and throw it on the table. Then he picked up his trench coat and hurried after her."

"About 10 minutes later, a departing customer found him lying by the rear of his car, shot dead. His key case was clutched in his hand, and the blood showed that he was shot where found. His wallet was gone, as were Thurston and her car."

"Did she own a gun?"

"No record of it, for what that's worth. The police picked her up at her home the next morning for questioning. She hasn't been arrested yet but remains the prime suspect, so she has retained Maryellen as a precaution. The police theory is that she waited for Lubbock near his car, either visibly or in the cedar hedge that lines the parking lot—the shot came from that direction—and then shot him, taking his wallet as a ruse, and fled."

"Hmmm." Stanwick swallowed some tea. "Is it certain that they arrived at the same time?"

"The driver of the car parked between them says so. Thurston parked her car nearer the inn door. The other diners confirmed the quarrel and their departure."

"I see." Stanwick set his mug down with a decisive thump. "I'm sure any associate of yours should be able to clear Thurston. She didn't shoot Lubbock."

How does Stanwick know that Thurston is innocent?

Solution on page 250

209

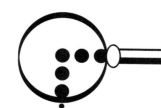

DEATH AT THE CLINIC

"IT'S YOUR BAD LUCK, old chum," said Thomas P. Stanwick, amateur logician, "that I recently made a special study of the Queen's Gambit Declined. That's when I found that innovation against your Cambridge Springs Defense that helped me win tonight."

Inspector Matthew Walker grunted. "Unfortunately, a working cop doesn't have time to keep up with your theoretical novelties. Good game, though."

Stanwick and Walker were relaxing in armchairs in the lounge of the Royston Chess Club following their weekly game. The windows were open to the warm evening air.

"How are Elizabeth and the boys?" asked Stanwick as he lit his pipe.

"Just fine, thanks," replied Walker. "When I left, Elizabeth was on the phone with one of her friends talking about their awful soap opera."

"'Awful soap opera' is not a very exclusive term. Which one?"

"'All My Nights.' An hour of guff. It's also popular, I've learned, in one of the best nutrition clinics in the city."

"Indeed?" Stanwick smiled and arched his eyebrows. "And how would a well-fed fellow like you know that?"

"A murder case. Dr. Mila Dixon runs a private clinic on the East End, and one of her nutritionists, Lola Alvarez, was shot to death last Wednesday."

"I see." Stanwick's face relaxed into pensiveness. "Any suspects? And what's the connection with 'All My Nights'?"

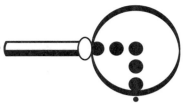

We have three suspects, all regular clients of Lola's. Malcolm Beard, a neurosurgeon, arrived just as 'All My Nights,' which begins at 1:30, was ending. He went into Lola's consulting room and hurried out, looking pale. One of the other nutritionists, Ellen Tiffany, shopped at Rosella's, a downtown boutique, for two hours after it opened and arrived back at the clinic half an hour later. Her arrival coincided with that of Frank McGowan, a building contractor. He was there exactly as long after the noon factory whistle four blocks away sounded as he was there before it."

"When does Rosella's open?"

"Nine."

"And the third suspect?"

"A personal-injury lawyer named Arthur Workman. Our witnesses have him arriving 45 minutes after McGowan left. He stayed half an hour to an hour."

Stanwick idly twisted the tip of his brown mustache.

"Interesting," he said. "Who discovered the body?"

"Mila, at about three. A silencer had been used on the gun. Lola was lying beside a tall scale. Beneath her was a smashed clock showing 1:44, which Doc Pillsbury says is consistent with the medical evidence as the time of death. The killer wasn't necessarily the last one to arrive, since any of them might have been too scared to report the body."

"Have you made the arrest yet?"

Walker shook his head. "We're still investigating."

"Fair enough." Stanwick tapped some ashes out of his pipe. "Assuming that the killer is one of your three suspects, however, a little deduction reveals which one it is."

Who murdered Lola Alvarez?

Solution on page 250

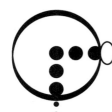

THE CASE OF
THE ROYSTON REINDEER

"THE SHOT probably came from one of the boats, Inspector!"

There were two at the mouth of the harbor: the *Dunfishin* and the *St. Elmo.* "Look for them!" An angry James Coughlin, attorney at law, stopped jabbing his finger, folded his arms, and sat back in his chair.

Across the table from him, Inspector Matthew Walker calmly picked up a sheet of paper.

"I have the ballistics report, counselor," he said. "Eleanor Freedman was shot by exactly the kind of rifle you are known to have possessed. She owned a successful hardware business and left a large estate and no family. As her attorney and executor, you have a financial interest in her death."

Coughlin snorted.

"Innuendo! I lost my rifle on a hunting trip in Central America five years ago. Got caught in a mudslide, and barely saved my neck. My rifle is still buried there somewhere."

"Were there witnesses to that?" asked Thomas P. Stanwick, the amateur logician, who was sitting in on the interrogation.

"No. My hunting companions caught up with me afterwards."

"Let's return to the events of last Thursday, Mr. Coughlin," said Walker. "Miss Freedman was taking a New Year's Day swim in the harbor at sunrise with 18 other members of the Royston Reindeer, who take that cold swim every year. You say you witnessed the swim from the 11th floor of your office building, about a block west of the harbor."

"That's right. I was high enough to have a direct view, and it was a clear morning."

"And you were working on New Year's Day?"

"I had an important deposition to prepare. No one else was there."

Half an hour later, Walker and Stanwick were down the hall in Walker's office.

"It's rather inconvenient for him that he can't produce his rifle for

testing or any witnesses to corroborate his alibi," remarked Stanwick.

"Yes," said Walker. "We're trying to trace those boats he mentioned. Because the swimmers were moving around, we can't be sure what direction or height the shot came from."

"The Royston Reindeer?" Stanwick smiled. "I knew reindeer could fly this time of year, but didn't know they could swim! At least Dasher and Dancer would live up to their names if thrown into icy water, no doubt. Anything interesting in the victim's effects?"

Walker shook his head. "She left her clothes, a robe, a towel, and her purse in the locker room of their clubhouse, as the others did. Oddly, she was the only one wearing a white bathing cap, which made her stand out. No shot was heard. The others thought she had had a heart attack or a seizure in the water."

"And Coughlin's office window would allow him to see the swimmers and the boats?"

"Oh, sure. The window opens, too, if you get my drift."

"I think I do." Stanwick idly fingered the tip of his droopy mustache. "I also think that Coughlin's alibi is a crock."

How does Stanwick know that Coughlin is lying?

Solution on page 251

MEMORIAL DAY MISCHIEF

THOMAS P. STANWICK was enjoying the annual Memorial Day festivities in his hometown of Baskerville.

The pancake breakfast in the armory had given the amateur logician a chance to catch up on local gossip. The parade up Main Street had started promptly at 10, and the flags, the veterans, the militia members in their colonial uniforms, and the school bands looked and sounded crisp. Civic leaders and town officials, and of course the Veteran of Honor, smiled and waved as they slowly marched down the street. The parade would be followed by a chicken barbecue in the playground.

Stanwick was viewing the parade from the sidewalk just outside Ollie's Army & Navy store. Just as a crack riflery unit was passing in front of him, the parade paused. For two minutes, in absolute silence, the riflers spun and tossed their rifles in complicated and exquisitely timed patterns. When they concluded, the band behind them struck up

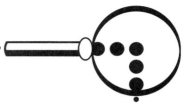

a march and the parade proceeded, to cheers and enthusiastic applause from the crowd.

A moment later, Stanwick heard a bellow of rage from the store just behind him. Entering it, Stanwick found the flushed-faced owner, Ollie Fortison, standing behind his sales counter holding an empty cash drawer from the register. Fortison, a burly former drill sergeant, glowered at four startled customers.

"What's wrong, Ollie?" asked Stanwick, walking up to him.

"This is what's wrong!" Fortison exclaimed, holding out the cash drawer. "This had over $300 in it five minutes ago, and now the bills are gone!"

"Please tell me what happened."

Fortison drew a long breath.

"It's simple enough, Tom," he said. "As you know, I stay open on Memorial Day until the parade is over, to sell flags or any last-minute items. I had just opened my cash drawer to sort my bills when the crowd outside grew quiet. Then I remembered that that out-of-town rifle unit was going to put on a show."

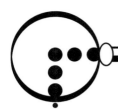

"I wanted to see it, so like a fool I left my cash drawer open and came to the window. At least a few of these customers did the same, but I didn't notice which ones. You could have heard a firing pin drop during the rifle display. When it was over, I came back to the counter and found the money gone!"

"And I heard your reaction on the sidewalk outside." Stanwick suppressed a grin. "Call the station, Ollie. And," he added, turning to the others, "I suggest that the rest of you remain until an officer arrives for your statements."

Stanwick was acquainted with two of the customers. One was Ellen Lilliott, a pretty brunette dressed in a tank top, shorts, and strap clogs, who owned a flower stand in town. The other was Paul Breen, a sandy-haired but balding executive in his 50s. Breen was dressed in an unholiday-like suit and wing-tip shoes. The two other customers were both young men, one with a military crew cut who was dressed in fatigues and boots, the other in a T-shirt, shorts, and sneakers.

A careful look around the store revealed nothing out of place to Stanwick. On display were clothes, camping goods, military paraphernalia, and various knickknacks. The hardwood floor was spit-and-polish as usual.

As soon as the sergeant had banged down the phone, Stanwick turned to him.

"Ollie," he said quietly, "could anyone have left the store since the theft?"

"Impossible! There's only one door, and its bell is in working order. You heard it when you came in. And no one else has been in here this morning."

"In that case," said Stanwick even more quietly, "make sure none of them leaves before the police arrive. Especially…"

Whom does Stanwick suspect of the theft, and why?

Solution on page 251

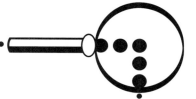

SABOTAGE AT CENTIPORE

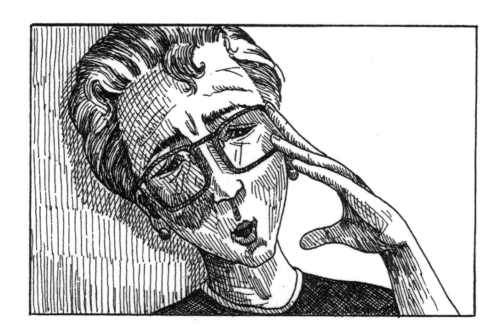

THE FOURTH FLOOR of the Centipore building, which housed the Engineering division, seldom had visitors. The medical membranes produced by Centipore were designed there, so the corporate security chief, Abraham Freedman, kept Engineering a restricted area.

Some tampering with a sensitive computer disk, however, had brought two visitors to the fourth floor. Inspector Matthew Walker and Thomas P. Stanwick were in the office of Sylvia DiCampli, the vice president of Engineering.

"The disk contains plans for a valuable membrane prototype, Inspector," DiCampli said. "It's kept in the storage room down the hall. The disk was fine when used last Wednesday, the 11th, but was found to be altered last Friday, the 13th. Harry Miller, the senior engineer who discovered the problem, reported it to me. I immediately confirmed it and reported it to Lester Parke, the executive vice president of Operations. He called your people."

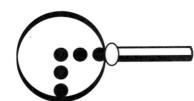

"Sergeant Hatch tells me that the door to the storage room was unforced," said Walker. "Therefore it was accessed by the swipe of a magnetic card. Please tell me who has access to that room."

"Besides myself and Harry Miller, that would be two other senior engineers, Tom Donlan and Chris Delaney, and Mr. Parke. Tom is new here, though, so for now he can get access to the room only with verification by one of the others."

"Couldn't Mr. Freedman authorize access for someone else?" asked Stanwick.

"Technically, yes," DiCampli replied, "but that would be highly irregular. Besides, he was laid up with the flu all last week, and conducted no business."

"I'd like another look at the room," said Walker, standing up.

A moment later, the three of them were in the small storage room. The walls were lined with shelves of floppy disk containers. DiCampli pointed out the container with the altered disk, which sat on a separate side shelf. A computer terminal rested on a small table against the center wall.

"Is the altered disk usually kept on that shelf?" asked Stanwick.

"That's right," replied DiCampli.

"And it was not altered on this terminal?"

"Correct. This terminal makes a note on its hard drive whenever it is used. We have verified the normal use on the 11th and the use on the 13th, when Harry discovered the problem. The disk was not used here between those times."

"You also told my sergeant that using the disk on another computer would require a decryption code," said Walker.

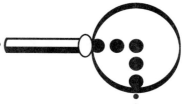

"Yes, and the code was changed on the 9th. It's issued automatically to senior engineers, and is available to me and higher-ups through Freedman."

"What damage to the company, Ms. DiCampli, could have resulted from the alteration of the disk?" asked Stanwick.

"It could have been worse. The alteration was discovered just in time to prevent a false patent application and costly failures in testing. Our competitors would have loved a delay in the discovery."

A short while later, Stanwick and Walker were eating lunch in the company cafeteria.

"Industrial espionage!" remarked Stanwick. "You don't often get those cases."

"True!" replied Walker with a rueful smile. "The chief still has me working as an Inspector Without Portfolio. It keeps my work varied."

"Anything interesting that you haven't told DiCampli?"

"In fact, yes," Walker leaned forward and spoke softly. "I have strong evidence that one of Centipore's competitors—one 10 times its size—selected, approached, and bribed at least one Centipore employee. We don't know which employee, though."

"Ah!" Stanwick took a pen and a pocket pad from his shirt pocket. "In that case, if all that DiCampli has told us checks out, I believe I can jot down who is responsible for the alteration of the disk."

Who altered the Centipore disk?

Solution on page 251

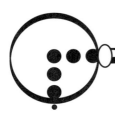

THE BRACKEN PARK INCIDENT

"SHE SAYS she never saw who attacked her," said Inspector Walker. "I've just come from the hospital. She's still pretty groggy, though, and may remember more later."

The inspector and Thomas P. Stanwick, the amateur logician, were striding briskly that crisp November morning through the streets of Royston toward Bracken Park. Earlier that morning, Alison Vaneer, a beautician in her early 30s, had been hit on the head and robbed while jogging through the park.

"When was she found?" asked Stanwick.

"About 8:30, by another jogger, just where the path passes a clump of trees. She was attacked a little after 7:00, just at daybreak. The money belt she wore around her stomach had been taken, and she was suffering from a concussion. For such chilly weather, she wasn't wearing

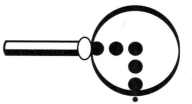

much: running shoes, a T-shirt, a tennis skirt, jacket with a reflector, a Harvard sweatshirt. And a baseball cap."

"Ah, a sedentary fellow like you wouldn't appreciate how warm some exercise can keep one," remarked Stanwick wryly.

Walker snorted. "And you would?"

They stopped by a news kiosk several yards from the south gate to the park.

"She entered the park through here," Walker said. "It's her usual route." With a flash of his badge, Walker introduced himself to the news dealer, Oscar Kramer.

"Did you see a woman jogger go into the park this morning?" he asked.

"A few actually," Kramer answered. "Which one?"

"The one with the Harvard sweatshirt," said Stanwick.

"Oh, yeah. Around seven, just as I was starting to open up. She's gone by every morning for the last couple of weeks, just like clock-work. Why?"

"She was attacked and robbed in the park," replied Walker impassively. "Did you see any suspicious persons enter or leave the park this way this morning?"

Kramer shook his head. "No, sir."

"Thank you," said Walker. "Sergeant Hatch will be along shortly to take your statement." He and Stanwick resumed their walk.

"Hatch is still at the crime scene," Walker told Stanwick as they entered the park. "It's about 50 yards up this way."

"I suggest he question Kramer carefully," said Stanwick with a frown. "That newsdealer could easily enough have anticipated Miss Vaneer's time and route, and lain in wait for her. He also knows more about this crime than he told us—no doubt of that!"

Why does Stanwick suspect the newsdealer of the crime?

Solution on page 251

THE CASE OF THE BULGARIAN DIAMONDS

THE POLYGRAPH EXAMINATION ROOM at Royston Police headquarters was conveniently fitted with a one-way mirror. In a small room behind this mirror stood Inspector Matthew Walker and his friend Thomas P. Stanwick, who was taking a break from his freelance editing to observe a slice of a criminal investigation.

"You may have seen something in the paper of the Bulgarian Diamond Mining Company securities scam," said Walker. "Over half a million 'invested' dollars were stolen. Of course, there was no such company."

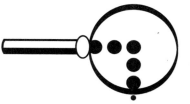

"And these four were involved?" asked Stanwick, peering through the glass into the polygraph room.

"That's right. Louis Lambert, Diane Sorensen, Morty Cameron, and John Thorpe ran the whole operation. One of the men was the salesman, another of the four printed the phony stock certificates, another kept the books, and the fourth acted as the banker, depositing and withdrawing the funds. We're questioning them now about their roles in the scam."

As Stanwick and Walker listened, the four suspects were given polygraph examinations. Each made two statements.

"I was the bookkeeper," declared Lambert. "You know what? Thorpe was the bookkeeper too!" He cackled with laughter.

"Lambert was not the banker," said Cameron. "I printed the certificates."

"Lambert wasn't the printer," Sorensen said. "The salesman was Thorpe."

"Either Diane or Morty kept the books," said Thorpe. "Diane doesn't know a thing about printing."

It was soon apparent that the four suspects would say no more, so Stanwick, who had been taking notes, departed. He returned the next day to visit Walker in his office. He found Walker glaring at the report of the polygraph examiner.

"I can't believe it!" Walker roared. "The polygraph is acting irregularly again. I'm told that each suspect made one true statement and one false statement, but that we can't tell which is which! I've got to persuade the chief to budget a new machine."

Stanwick laughed heartily.

"I hear that polygraphs are notoriously unreliable," he said. "If that report is true, though, a little logic can determine which statements were true, which were false, and who played what role in the scam!"

Who did what in the Bulgarian Diamond Mining Company?

Solution on page 252

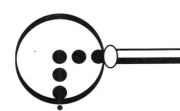

ONE MORNING AT THE FESTIVAL

THE VILLAGE OF Knordwyn in Northumbria, England, was celebrating its annual Queen Anne Festival. For several August days, people from around the shire came to enjoy craft displays, athletic competitions, farm shows, and cooking and music contests.

Also attending the festival was Thomas P. Stanwick, the amateur logician. He visited the village every year or two, and found

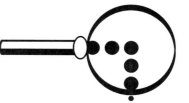

Knordwynians invariably intriguing: about one half were lifelong liars, and the rest were lifelong truthtellers. Conversations with them were thus real tests of his skill at deduction.

On the second festival day, Stanwick arrived at the grounds early to see the pigs. He was curious to see a particularly hefty specimen named Miss Porky Pine (because of her prickly disposition, according to a wag at the village pub). When he reached the stalls, however, he found hers empty and her owner, Ian Craigmore, angrily questioning three men and a woman. Upon seeing Stanwick, Craigmore turned to him.

"Tom, my lad," he sputtered, "someone stole Miss Porky Pine from her stall last night. It must have been one thief: she is nervous and squeals loudly if two try to handle her."

"And you suspect these four?"

"Yes. Charles Hagman, Thomas Leary, and Dora Glasker are festival attendants, and Louis Parrella was cooking a suspiciously early barbecue not far from the festival grounds, so I brought him over. All four are from the village."

Stanwick knew Craigmore to be a villager and a truthteller. Turning to the suspects, he asked if they could tell him anything about the theft.

"Louis never attends the festival," said Hagman. "Also, Thomas and Dora are not both truthtellers."

"Dora stole the pig," announced Leary. "She and Louis are both liars."

Glasker cleared her throat angrily. "Neither Charles nor Thomas is the thief," she said. "Louis attends the festival every other year."

"Either Dora or Thomas is a liar," stated Parrella. "The thief, however, is not Charles or Dora."

Stanwick smiled pleasantly.

"In an admittedly indirect way," he said, "You've been very helpful. And now," he continued, turning to one of them, "perhaps you could tell us why you stole the portly pig."

Who stole Miss Porky Pine?

Solution on page 252

CHIEF RYAN PAYS A CALL

CHIEF WILLIAM RYAN of the Baskerville Police was exchanging local gossip with Thomas P. Stanwick one afternoon in the living room of Stanwick's bungalow. Stanwick's black Labrador, Rufus, slept peacefully in a patch of sunlight.

"I think the Sherman lad will turn out all right," concluded the chief, a taciturn man with thinning hair. "I had a long talk with him. He won't go wrong again."

"That's good to hear, Chief," said Stanwick. "The Shermans are a fine family. Do you have any interesting investigations going on these days?"

"Actually, we do. Three local stores—Fine Jewels, Harrigan's Hardware, and the Gasco Mart—have been robbed by a small gang of teen-

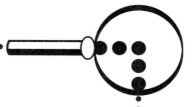

agers over the last two months. The same gang has hit stores in two other nearby towns. The four teens in the gang are students from the Baskerville and Royston high schools, so we've been running a joint investigation with the Royston police."

"Who's in charge of the Royston end?" asked Stanwick. "Matt Walker?"

"No. Inspector Martinez."

Stanwick nodded. "She's very capable."

"Anyway, we've identified the four. The Baskerville students are Lisa Janison and Tony Aronisi. Fred Wynant and Joyce Bobbin are from Royston. We have them under surveillance, but we want to learn more about them before we make any arrests.

"We especially want to learn what nicknames they call each other, and how they rank themselves within the group," the chief went on. "One of them is called Muscle. The one in charge is of course called Leader. Bobbin, we find, outranks Wynant but is not the leader. Aronisi is called Driver. (Guess what his job is!) The one called Weapons, who is not Wynant, is ranked just below Leader. We also know that Driver is not the lowest-ranked position. We need more than these bits and pieces, though, to sort out who is who in what order of rank. Only then will we be ready to take them to court."

Stanwick smiled and slowly filled his pipe.

"I've been up to my elbows in a geometry manuscript all day," he remarked genially, "and I thought your visit, no offense, would give me a break from deductive reasoning. Alas, no! I think I can prove, in fact, that the 'bits and pieces' you cite are enough to give you the information you want."

Which gang member has what nickname and rank?

Solution on page 252

THE POWERS' PREDICAMENT

"THANK YOU KINDLY," said Thomas P. Stanwick, leaning forward in his chair to accept more tea and another piece of cake from Genevieve Hardis. "You must be looking forward to seeing your family next week for Thanksgiving."

"Yes, indeed, my boy," replied Ron Hardis, a grin creasing his strong jaw. "We're going out to Charlie's, in upstate New York."

"Our three children and their families will all be there," Gen Hardis said as she sat down.

Stanwick was in the living room visiting the elderly but vigorous Hardises. "Thanksgiving came on fast this year," he said. "Pretty soon, every corner will have a Santa ringing a bell."

"That's right," said Gen. "We give to a few charities, and the Christmas appeals have already begun to arrive in the mail. One came the other day from an outfit we never heard of, 'Family Help Today.'"

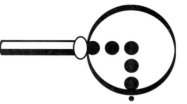

"Hmmm. That's new to me, too," said Stanwick. "May I see it?"

"Here it is," said Ron, taking a letter from an end table and handing it to Stanwick. "It's from someone named Arnold Creelman, 'regional coordinator,' asking for help for a homeless family."

Stanwick settled back to read the letter.

"Dear RON HARDIS:

"This holiday season, a generous citizen like you will want to assist your needy neighbors in BASKERVILLE. Let me introduce you to the Powers family. Frank Powers, a former Navy flier, is now disabled and can do only odd jobs. He, his wife Maryann, who is unemployed, and their two children, Marjorie, 11, and Robbie, 8, are living in their station wagon, with their few goods piled in the back.

"In spite of their difficulties, Marjorie and Robbie attend school and do their homework in the BASKERVILLE public library. They sneak showers in the school gym when they can. At night, the family sleeps in the car with the heat on to keep warm.

"Can you help the members of the Powers family get back on their feet? They distrust homeless shelters, which you will agree are not good places for children. RON HARDIS, your contribution this holiday season will be much appreciated."

Stanwick smiled and put down the letter.

"How charmingly personal," he said. "I suggest you find worthier causes for your giving. On at least two counts, this appeal is a fraud."

How does Stanwick know that the charity appeal is a fraud?

Solution on page 253

AN IDYLL DAY IN EDINBURGH

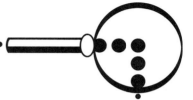

THOMAS P. STANWICK, the amateur logician, was on vacation in Edinburgh and had spent most of an idyllic autumn afternoon browsing in musty bookshops. Shortly before dusk, he visited a small shop off a crooked lane. He had just opened a book on medieval Scottish theology when he heard the sharp voice of the elderly shop owner directed at a goateed man at the door.

"Excuse me, sir," said the owner, "but did you not forget to pay me for the Anderson book in your hand?"

"Why, no, sir," replied the customer, stepping back inside. "I bought this last week at another shop—for less than your price, I may add—and had it with me when I came in here."

"No, no, I'm sure this is mine," said the owner, walking up to the customer and pointing toward his shelves. "You see the gap in that shelf there? I have only the one copy, and have not sold it."

"You must be mistaken, sir. Perhaps you simply forgot selling it."

"I think not. Excuse me." The owner turned over the cover. "Ah! As you can see, there are erasure marks in the corner of the inside page, where I always note the price in pencil. You have erased it!"

"All bookshops put the price there," snapped the customer. "I erased it after I got the book home last week."

"Have you a receipt for this?"

"Not anymore. I threw it away days ago. Did you not see me enter with the book?"

"No, but my back was turned when you came in, I must confess."
"Well, then," said the customer, turning away. "I'll be on my way."

"I beg your pardon," said Stanwick. He walked up and addressed the customer. "It would be cumbersome to call in the police, who could search you for an eraser, possibly on a pencil, or search the shop for one you might have discarded. You have already incriminated yourself, however, so perhaps you would be willing to make restitution to this gentleman privately instead."

How did the customer incriminate himself?

Solution on page 253

ROOM AT THE INN

DUSK WAS GATHERING as Thomas P. Stanwick, the amateur logician, arrived in Knordwyn at the end of a 15-mile hike. He was fond of visiting the tiny Northumbrian village when he was on vacation in England. About half its inhabitants always lied, and the rest always told the truth. His conversations with them were thus stimulating exercises in deduction.

With a sigh of relief, Stanwick threw off this backpack and sat down heavily on a bench by the village green. His immediate concern was to find a room for the night. Three villagers were passing by just then, and he hailed them.

"Excuse me," he asked, "but are there any rooms available at the Grey Boar Inn tonight?"

"Yes, there are," said the first villager.

"Either no rooms are available," said the second villager, "or he and I are both liars."

"Either two of us are liars," added the third villager, "or the first fellow is telling the truth."

"Thank you," said Stanwick with a weary smile. He was used to the sometimes wildly indirect answers of the villagers. These three had said enough, however, for him to deduce who was lying and, more important, whether there was room at the inn.

Who was lying? Is there room at the inn?

Solution on page 253

232

STANWICK SOLVES A PIE PUZZLE

ON THE FIRST SATURDAY of each May, Baskerville held its annual Craft & Bake Fair on the large, open playground behind the elementary school. In colorful booths and tents were displayed handmade stitchery and sculpture, along with home-baked breads, cookies, cakes, and pies.

Thomas P. Stanwick always enjoyed the chance to buy delectables and to see friends and neighbors at the fair. This year, however, an investigation in Royston kept him from the fairgrounds until late in the afternoon. Once there, he visited several displays.

His last stop was a large, open tent that had several tables of baked goods.

Three elderly ladies named Frieda, Gertie, and Hazel were behind one table talking busily among themselves. The table had a cherry pie in the center and a blueberry pie in the back right corner. Stanwick knew all three women and greeted them cheerily.

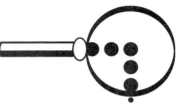

"Good day, ladies!" he said. "Only two pies left, I see. Whose are they?"

"Why, Thomas," replied Frieda, "we were just trying to remember that ourselves, so that the unsold pies can go home with their bakers. We each made an apple, a blueberry, and a cherry, you see, but didn't label them by owner. The sale money went into the charity pot."

"So you had nine pies, and sold seven," said Stanwick. "How were they placed on the table?"

"We had three rows of three pies each," replied Gertie. "Each row had one of each type of pie. Only one or two of my pies were sold."

"Each of us had one pie in the front row," said Hazel. "Gertie had two pies in the middle row, I remember. I also remember that my apple and my blueberry were sold. I'm not sure about my cherry."

Stanwick chuckled as he took out his wallet.

"The question is moot," he said, "since I will buy the two remaining pies. They look delicious. With the help of a little logic, however, I can tell you who baked them."

Who baked which of the remaining pies?

Solution on page 254

STANWICK AT CHARTWELL

THOMAS P. STANWICK had always been a great admirer of Winston Churchill. When traveling in England in the summertime, the amateur logician enjoyed visiting Chartwell, Churchill's home near Westerham. Over the years, he had become acquainted with several of the National Trust staffers who maintained it.

On this occasion, Stanwick was sitting on a bench overlooking the estate's lake and the green Kent hillsides, chatting with Niles Archer. A soft-spoken man with thick-framed glasses, Archer was one of the Chartwell administrators.

"Has Chartwell had a good flow of visitors this summer, Niles?" asked Stanwick.

"Oh, yes," Archer replied. "We've been busy. We've also had an unusual number of special tours. The Churchill family is especially interested in these, so one of my duties is to prepare a weekly report on

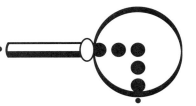

them. This week, unfortunately, my report will be a bit patchy."

"No special tours this week?"

"Oh, no, we've had five already. The bad luck is, I have mislaid my notes on the history club that visited us yesterday afternoon. I do remember that there were four members: Elaine Thompson, Albert Martin, Bill Colville, and Ellen Pearman. They came from Oldham, Epping, Dundee, and Woodford, though I forget in which order. One was a bricklayer, another was an historian, another was a novelist, and the fourth was a landscape painter, but again I forget which was which."

"That's remarkable!" Stanwick laughed. "How appropriate that such a group should visit Chartwell. Their names are those of important assistants to Churchill. They come from towns that Churchill represented in Parliament. And their occupations reflect some of Churchill's own occupations and hobbies."

"Why, so they do!" Archer smiled. "Thank you, Thomas. That had not occurred to me. Those points can help salvage my report."

"Can you remember anything more about the group?"

"Well, let me see. The woman from Dundee was neither the painter nor the bricklayer. Mr. Martin, of Epping, despised writing of any kind. Mrs. Pearman was not, I believe, from Woodford. The historian was a bachelor from Oldham. And I gained the distinct understanding that Miss Thompson did not work with a trowel."

"Well done, Niles!" exclaimed Stanwick with a grin. "With a little deduction, your report can yet be made complete. If you'll join me over a cup of tea, I'll jot down who did what where."

Can you match the visitors with their occupations and towns?

Solution on page 254

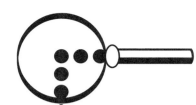

THE TALE OF
THE GENEROUS RAJAH

AN ARMCHAIR in the reading room of Baskerville Public Library proved too comfortable a place for Thomas P. Stanwick at four o'clock on a warm afternoon. His eyes slid closed, his head slumped to his chest, and the book slipped from his fingers to the floor.

The head librarian, who had seen these symptoms before, walked quietly over to the amateur logician and gently shook his shoulder.

"Mr. Stanwick! You haven't fallen asleep, have you, sir?" she asked.

Stanwick snapped to alertness.

"What?" he said. "Oh, hello, Mrs. Mitten. Good Lord, I wasn't snoring, was I?"

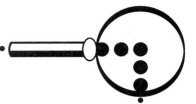

"No, no. I caught you in time."

"Thank you." Stanwick sheepishly picked up the book. "It's no reflection on what I was reading. Have you seen the memoirs of Morton Henry Stanley? He was a British explorer who traveled from Bombay across the Thar Desert to the northern reaches of India in the early 1800s."

"No, I don't think I've heard the name." Intrigued, the librarian sat down in the chair beside Stanwick's and examined the book closely.

"Stanley had many interesting adventures," Stanwick went on. "In one, he missed an excellent chance of gaining a large fortune in precious stones."

"Do go on," the librarian said.

Stanwick settled back in his chair and toyed with the tip of his droopy mustache.

"Well, as you probably know," he recounted, "India in those days had many independent kingdoms, or *raji*, each ruled by a fierce rajah. During one of his journeys, Stanley was captured by one of these rajahs. The rajah found his prisoner to be a fascinating conversationalist. (Stanley was a gifted linguist and knew several Indian dialects.) They discussed local politics and world events, and played many games of chess.

"That night the rajah presided over an elaborate dinner, which was, according to his custom, to have been followed by the execution of the trespasser. The rajah, however, announced that he would give Stanley an opportunity to leave the raji unharmed and even wealthy.

"Three large chests were brought in to the center of the dining hall. Each was lavishly bound and secured by a huge lock. A besotted servant then stumbled in carrying three signs, one picturing a diamond, another picturing a ruby, and the third picturing an emerald. The fellow first put the emerald sign on the first trunk. After a confused pause, he then took that sign off the first trunk and put it on the second trunk. Finally, after some fumbling, he put the diamond sign on the first trunk and the ruby sign on the third trunk. Then he staggered out.

"'You must forgive my servant,' laughed the rajah, turning to his guest of honor. 'He has taken a little too much hashish today. I am afraid that in none of his attempts did he succeed in putting the correct sign on the correct chest. Nonetheless, one chest does contain diamonds, another contains rubies, and another emeralds.

"Each chest has a rather complicated lock. Here is a golden lock-pick. I will give you five minutes to open one of the chests. Seeing its contents should enable you to divine the contents of all three chests. If you succeed in divining this, you may have all three chests and their contents, and safe passage to the border. If you fail, I fear I must proceed with the execution. You may begin.'

"Stanley needed no further prompting. Snatching up the lock-pick, he hurried over to the three chests, paused briefly, and then began furiously picking at the lock of the middle chest, the one with the emerald sign. As the rajah chuckled quietly, Stanley muttered to himself and wrestled with the lock. Beads of sweat glistened on his forehead as the rajah called time. With a curse, Stanley flung the pick to the ground and glared at the still impregnable lock.

"The rajah laughed heartily at the spectacle of the explorer's fury and frustration.

"'Such a pity!' he exclaimed. 'I fear that the lock was too stubborn for you.'

"'Just tell me what is in one of these chests, good rajah,' said Stanley, 'and I will indeed tell you what is in the other two.'

"'I am sure you could, my friend,' replied the rajah. 'But fear not. You have entertained me well today, so I will spare your life and reward you for your company.'

"The rajah then made good on his word by giving our relieved hero a small bagful of precious stones and a mounted escort to the border of the raji."

Stanwick grinned slyly. Mrs. Mitten, who had a weakness for

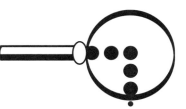

tales of adventure in exotic lands, remained lost in thought for a moment.

"It's a shame that he couldn't open the lock," she said at last. "I think I see how he could then have deduced the contents of all three chests, if all the signs were put on wrong."

"Quite true!" said Stanwick with a laugh. "Poor Stanley, however, was not quite astute enough to guess the real cause of the rajah's amusement. If only the brave explorer had been a little more alert, he might have realized that he had the power to 'divine' the contents of all three chests without touching the lock-pick at all."

How could Stanley have done this?

Solution on page 254

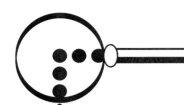

THE CASE OF THE CONTENTIOUS COWS

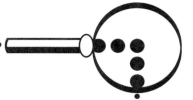

WITH A PACK on his back and a staff in his hand, Thomas P. Stanwick strode down a gently sloping hill as he followed Route 221. The amateur logician, weary after many weeks of editing a long geometry textbook and helping Inspector Walker solve crimes, was enjoying a summer walking tour in Vermont. He was now about 12 miles from Greenfield Inn, where he would spend the night.

As Stanwick approached the bottom of the hill, he observed several cows behind a gate on the left and a farm lad staring at them from the road side of the gate. Some of the cows were black, some were brown, and all had white patches. The boy, who was about 16, wore a dirty cap, a T-shirt, and a pair of old jeans. He continued to scowl at the cows as Stanwick came up to him.

"Good morning," said Stanwick, pausing to chat. "Fine weather. Time to bring the cows across?"

The boy grunted. "Ain't quite that easy, though," he muttered.

"No? Why not?"

"These are peculiar cows, Mister. The black ones are real nasty, and will butt and bite the brown ones if they outnumber 'em and I ain't right there."

"Can't you just bring them all across at once?"

"Nope. Only two at a time. Gotta hold 'em by the collar or they trot away up the road."

"They are peculiar cows!" remarked Stanwick with a grin. "You have four black ones and three brown ones, I see."

"I've been tryin' for an hour to get these cows across," the boy blurted out angrily, "and every way I try, I leave more black cows than brown cows alone on one side of the road or the other! Can you give me a hand, Mister?"

"I'm afraid I'm not much good at handling cows myself," Stanwick said. "I think I can show you a way, though, to get the cows across without leaving more black ones than brown ones together unattended."

How can the cows be brought safely across the road?

Solution on page 255

BABIES FOR THE BULLETIN

"GOOD MORNING, LOUISE!" exclaimed Thomas P. Stanwick as he and Rufus entered the church office. "Mind if a man and his dog drop by to say hello?"

Louise Muller, the church secretary, looked up with a start and smiled.

"Why, not at all," she replied. "It's nice to see you, Tom. And you too, Rufus." She patted the black Labrador as he sat beside her.

"I'll try not to sneeze," Stanwick said with a grin. "With so many slips of paper on your desk, any air disturbance might delay your finishing the bulletin for a month!"

"That could hardly make it worse right now," said Muller with a small sigh. "It's so embarrassing, Tom! Four babies were born to members within the last couple of weeks, on March 27, March 30, April 2, and April 4. Two are little girls (Jennifer and Lucile) and two are little boys (Frederick and Wolfgang). I'm supposed to put their full names, birthdates, and birth weights in the bulletin, but my notes got mixed up. And I would feel silly to have to go to the parents about it! But I suppose I'll have to."

"I see." Stanwick sat down in a chair beside the desk and looked over the note slips. "Are these the last names? Sartorius, Shirley, Wagner, and Lee?"

"That's right. And the weights are 5 pounds, 5 ounces; 6 pounds, 7 ounces; 7 pounds, 8 ounces; and 5 pounds, 15 ounces."

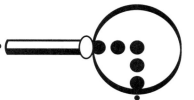

"Do you have any information that might help sort this out?"

"Well, some." The secretary gathered a few of the slips. "Jennifer was born in March. The Sartorius boy was born on April 4. At least two of the babies are heavier than Frederick. The heaviest baby was born two days later than the Shirley baby, and the Wagner girl was born three days before the baby that weighed six pounds and seven ounces."

"Hmmm." Stanwick frowned. "Anything more?"

"Well, I remember that the smallest baby was either the first or the last one born. Oh, and the Lee baby was not eight ounces lighter than the Shirley baby, who is not Frederick."

Stanwick laughed.

"You certainly have an eclectic memory, Louise," he said. "If it's accurate, however, we have enough information to match the names, dates, and weights for the bulletin announcements."

What is the full name, birthdate, and weight of each baby?

Solution on page 255

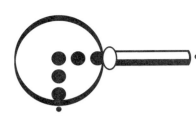

STANWICK AT THE CIRCUS

THE APPEARANCE one summer morning of a large tent in the south-east corner of the Baskerville playground could mean only one thing: the Richard Brothers one-ring circus was back in town.

Early that morning, Thomas P. Stanwick and his Labrador, Rufus, were walking among the stalls, trailers, and piles of equipment and canvas that constitute the impedimenta of even a small circus. The amateur logician admired the almost military precision with which the company of performers and crew set the circus up.

"Good morning, dear sir!" said a voice behind him.

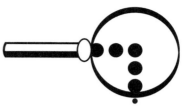

Stanwick turned to see a cheery man with white hair and a florid face, wearing a baggy black suit, an elaborate bow tie, a silk hat, and a vest with a watch chain.

"Professor McFuddle!" exclaimed Stanwick, shaking his hand. "Welcome back. How is everyone at Richard Brothers?"

"Just fine, Thomas," McFuddle replied with a laugh. "Of course, since Wanda the Contortionist ran off to join an accounting firm, Mr. Richard has been trying to reorganize the acts. It's had him perplexed, I don't mind telling you."

"Why is that?"

"Well, Delpho the Acrobat and Jilko the Juggler demand the same amount of time for their acts. (A bit of professional jealousy there.) Carlo, the elephant trainer, won't go on first, but insists on going on before Delpho. He also needs three times as much time as Delpho.

"Bobo the Clown needs only half as much time as Carlo," the professor continued, "but he refuses to be the last of the four to go on. Of the four, Jilko goes on third. There are some other acts, including mine, that take a total of 46 minutes. The whole show lasted two and a half hours."

"And Mr. Richard, I suppose, is trying to accommodate the performers by putting them in the right order," said Stanwick.

"Exactly. He is also trying to make sure he can give them each enough time."

Stanwick whistled to Rufus, who was starting to wander.

"Well, Professor," he said, "if it isn't too early to see Mr. Richard, I think I can point out an order of performance the performers can live with and how much time each will require. The show must go on!"

How much time will each act need, and in what order?

Solution on page 256

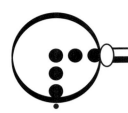

SOLUTIONS

The Stockbroker's Last Morning (page 185)

Golding said Steinberg was seized with convulsions as soon as the coffee cup left his lips, and that no one had been in the room since his death. If this were true, the coffee cup would not have been placed back on the saucer, where Stanwick found it.

Golding had actually entered Steinberg's office from his own office while Steinberg was sipping his coffee and reading the paper in the easy chair. Engaging Steinberg in conversation, Golding slipped poison from the vial into the coffee. Steinberg drank it and died. Golding then (erroneously) replaced the cup, refolded the paper, and put it aside. Wiping his prints from the vial, he put Steinberg's prints on it and put it in the dead man's pocket. He then typed the suicide note (wearing gloves), went back into his office through the connecting door, entered the reception area, picked up the newsletter documents, and enacted his version of the tragedy.

Golding eventually confessed to murdering his mentor to advance his own career.

A Model Murder (page 188)

Phillips was the killer.

Walker had told him only that Lola had been found dead in the house. Without being the killer, Phillips would not have known when he entered the house that she had been stabbed upstairs.

Phillips' trial revealed that Lola had broken off with him during their lunch. He had killed her out of jealousy and was convicted of the crime.

The Adventure of the Negative Clue (page 191)

If Orrison had just finished slicing fish all morning, he would have retained a noticeable odor of fish, especially on a warm day. While Walker was questioning him, however, the shop had only a metallic odor. The absence of a sharp fish odor was the negative clue.

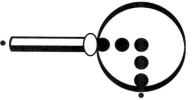

The Case of the Invisible Murderer (page 195)

The circumstances of Hottleman's death make suicide or natural death impossible, so he was murdered. The murderer must have entered the room through the main doorway after Hottleman reentered it following his return of the sunglasses.

Stanwick's main clue was the condition of the tables in the murder room. Only the victim's table still had dirty utensils and dishes. The others, including whichever table the elderly couple had used, had been cleared. Nothing had been touched after the discovery of the body, so the tables must have been cleared before then but after the couple had left. Only one person could have done this without seeming out of place or attracting even the slightest notice from the preoccupied owner: the "invisible" busboy. The busboy was therefore the murderer.

Subsequent investigation by Walker proved that Stanwick's deduction was correct. The busboy had murdered the wealthy Hottleman for his wallet.

Death Brings Down the Curtain (page 199)

Stanwick noticed that the movements of the first "victim," Mort Hooper, were not independently confirmed. His character having been shot, he would not have had to reappear on stage until the curtain call, so no one else cared where he was until then. He was therefore the prime suspect, and was eventually found to have committed the crime out of obsessive jealousy.

A Death by the Thames (page 202)

The maid mentioned the missing silver and jewels. She could have seen the rifled silver case, which was in the living room, but could not have known about the jewels missing from the bedroom if, as she claimed, she had only been in the living room before fleeing the flat.

Miss Woolbrott eventually confessed that she had helped her boyfriend ransack the flat, and that he had killed Sir Alan when the industrialist returned home unexpectedly early.

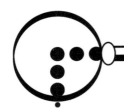

The Table of Death (page 204)

Stanwick deduced that a man planning to take part in a suicide would not bother to fold and put away a gasoline receipt, but that a salesman expecting to live and write the expense off his income taxes would.

Barnes secretly poisoned Hunter during a cult ritual, and then prepared the "suicide" note and poisoned himself.

Murder at Big Jake's (page 206)

Since he was identified at the bar, Gummond's first statement is false. Under either variation of the disorder, his second statement is therefore true. The content of that statement implies the truth of the fourth statement as well.

If Gummond were lying every third statement, his fourth statement (three after the false first statement) would be false, which it isn't. Thus he is lying every other statement. Gummond's third statement is therefore false, and he did the shooting.

Murder by the Wayward (page 208)

Since Lubbock died by his car with his key case in his hand, he was preparing to drive away, probably in pursuit of Thurston. If he had seen her or her parked car, he would have approached her or looked for her instead.

He was shot from the direction of the hedge. She could therefore have shot him only by moving her car out of sight and then returning to hide and wait for him. He left the inn so soon after she did, however, that there was not enough time for that. She therefore did not shoot him.

Death at the Clinic (page 210)

McGowan arrived two and a half hours after Rosella's opened, at 11:30 A.M. He was there half an hour before and after the noon whistle, and so left at 12:30 P.M. Workman arrived 45 minutes later, at 1:15 P.M., and stayed at least half an hour. Since Lola died at 1:44 P.M., he was the killer.

Beard arrived at 2:30 P.M., at the end of an hour-long soap opera that began at 1:30 P.M., found Lola dead, and left.

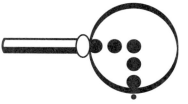

The Case of the Royston Reindeer (page 212)

Coughlin's office was west of the harbor, so he was looking into the harbor on a clear day, facing the newly rising sun. Though he would have been able to see the swimmers and probably even any boats, the glare and shadows would have made impossible his reading the names of the boats from a distance.

Memorial Day Mischief (page 214)

Stanwick suspected the young man in the T-shirt. Only he had the sort of footwear (sneakers) that would have been quiet enough on a hardwood floor for him to have committed the crime in absolute silence.

Sabotage at Centipore (page 217)

The records of the storage room terminal establish that the alteration was done on an outside computer, which required the use of a decryption code. Anyone other than the senior engineers would have had to get the new code through Freedman, who was out sick all that week. Therefore one of the senior engineers altered the disk.

If Miller were the culprit, he would have at least delayed his pretended discovery. The competitor thus selected Donlan or Delaney. Selecting Donlan would have been pointless, however, since he would have needed the cooperation of one of the others. He could not enter the storage room alone, and the location of the disk there would have made it very difficult for him to remove it without the accompanying engineer being aware of it. The selected, and guilty, engineer is therefore Delaney.

The Bracken Park Incident (page 220)

Stanwick suspected Kramer because the news vendor claimed to recognize the victim when Stanwick mentioned the Harvard sweatshirt. Miss Vaneer had also worn a jacket with a reflector, which of course would have been worn over the sweatshirt. The vendor would therefore not have known what the sweatshirt looked like unless he had been the attacker, who had to open the jacket to get to the money belt around her stomach.

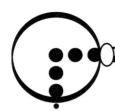

Even if Vaneer had worn the sweatshirt on previous jogs, Kramer would by his statement have seen her only during the previous two weeks, when the seasonal chill would still have required her to wear the same layers of clothing.

The Case of the Bulgarian Diamonds (page 222)

If Thorpe's first statement (T1) is true, then both of Lambert's statements (L1 and L2) are false. This contradicts the premise that each made one true and one false statement, so T1 is false and T2 is true. Therefore neither Sorenson nor Cameron was the bookkeeper, and Sorensen was not the printer. Since she was not the salesman either (the salesman having been one of the men), she must have been the banker. This means that C1 is true, so C2 is false and Cameron was not the printer. He must therefore be the salesman.

This proves that S2 is false, so S1 is true and Lambert was not the printer. Lambert was therefore the bookkeeper, and Thorpe was the printer.

One Morning at the Festival (page 224)

If Hagman were a liar, then Leary and Glasker would both be truthtellers. Glasker would also be a liar, because of Leary's second statement. Since this is impossible, Hagman is a truthteller. Parrella therefore never attends the festival, so Glasker is a liar. Since Parrella's first statement is a restatement of Hagman's second statement, Parrella is also a truthteller.

Since Glasker is a liar, by her first statement, the thief must be either Hagman or Leary. By Parrella's second statement, however, Hagman is not the thief. The thief is therefore Leary.

When presented with this reasoning, Leary confessed to stealing Miss Porky Pine for culinary reasons. She was returned intact.

Chief Ryan Pays a Call (page 226)

Leader, who has the highest rank, is not Wynant, who is outranked, or Bobbin (given), or Aronisi (Driver), and therefore is Janison. Weapons is not Wynant (given), or Janison (Leader), or Aronisi (Driver), and therefore is Bobbin. Wynant by elimination is Muscle.

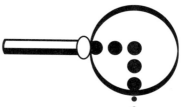

Leader has the highest rank, so Weapons, just below Leader, is second. Driver does not have the lowest rank, and thus is third. Muscle therefore is fourth.

The Powers' Predicament (page 228)

Stanwick knew that the family could not repeatedly sleep in the car with the motor running (which would be necessary for the heat to work) without likely being asphyxiated by carbon monoxide. This is the first flaw.

The capitalized words in the letter (indicating the name and town of the recipient) would also change with each letter recipient. Presumably the Powers children would study in the same library each day. The location of the library, however, was in capitals (the second flaw), and would therefore vary with each letter.

An Idyll Day in Edinburgh (page 230)

The customer said he had bought the book for a lower price at another shop. If this were so, however, he would not have known what the present shop owner charged for the book, since there were no other copies in the shop. He would only have known the shop owner's price by seeing it in the book in the present shop before erasing it.

Room at the Inn (page 232)

If the first villager is telling the truth, then the second villager is lying, and if the first villager is lying, then the second villager is telling the truth.

Now suppose the third villager is lying. Then the first clause of his statement would be true (since he and one of the other two would be liars). His disjunctive statement as a whole would then be true, which is impossible for a liar. Therefore the third villager is telling the truth. His first clause is therefore false (since only one of the three can be lying), so for his statement as a whole to be true, his second clause must be true.

Therefore the first and third villagers are telling the truth, the second villager is lying, and there is room at the inn.

Stanwick Solves a Pie Puzzle (page 234)

At least one of the remaining pies was baked by Gertie, who had sold only one or two. She had had one pie in the front row and two in the middle row, so the blueberry pie in the back row could not have been hers. She had therefore baked the cherry pie in the center.

The blueberry pie in the back was not baked by Gertie or by Hazel, who had sold hers. It was therefore baked by Frieda.

Stanwick at Chartwell (page 236)

The bachelor historian from Oldham was one of the two men, but not Martin (who hated to write), and thus was Colville.

Pearman was not from Woodford, Epping (Martin), or Oldham (Colville), and so was from Dundee. She therefore was not the painter, the bricklayer, or the historian (Colville), and so was the novelist.

Thompson, who must by elimination have come from Woodford, could not have laid bricks without a trowel, so she must have been the painter, leaving Martin as the bricklayer.

In summary: Thompson was the painter from Woodford; Martin was the bricklayer from Epping; Colville was the historian from Oldham; and Pearman was the novelist from Dundee.

The Tale of the Generous Rajah (page 238)

Morton Henry Stanley was correct in asserting that, if he could know what was in one chest, all of which were mislabeled, he could deduce what was in the other two. Suppose he had succeeded in opening the middle chest, the one with the emerald sign. It would have contained either diamonds or rubies. If it had contained diamonds, then the rubies would have been in the chest with the diamond sign and the emeralds would have been in the chest with the ruby sign. If it had instead contained rubies, then the diamonds would have been in the chest with the ruby sign and the emeralds would have been in the chest with the diamond sign. Only by these combinations could all three chests have the wrong signs. Had he chosen and opened one of the other two chests, similar reasoning would have revealed the contents of all three.

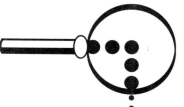

Unfortunately for the good explorer, he failed to notice that the rajah had said that the befuddled servant had failed in each of his attempts to match a sign to the right chest. As Stanwick noticed, there were in fact four such attempts, the first being when the servant put the emerald sign on the first trunk. Only after that did he arrange the signs in their final order (diamond-emerald-ruby). This meant that the first trunk contained neither the emeralds nor the diamonds. It therefore contained the rubies. Since the second chest had the emerald sign, the emeralds must have been in the third chest, and the diamonds must have been in the second.

The offer of a lock-pick was therefore an unnecessary ruse. Stanwick knew this, but Morton Henry Stanley never suspected it.

The Case of the Contentious Cows (page 243)

To meet the conditions of the problem, Stanwick suggested the following sequence: 1) Take a black cow across. 2) Take a black cow and a brown cow across, and bring a black cow back. 3) Take two brown cows across. 4) Take two black cows across. 5) Take the last black cow across.

Babies for the Bulletin (page 244)

Since there is only one two-day gap in the dates, the Shirley baby was born on April 2, and the seven-pound, eight-ounce baby was born on April 4 and is therefore the Sartorius boy. The smallest (five pounds, five ounces) baby was not born on April 4, so he or she was born on March 27. The Sartorius boy is not Frederick (who is not the heaviest baby) and is therefore Wolfgang.

The Shirley baby is not Jennifer (born in March) or Frederick (given) or Wolfgang (born April 4), and so is Lucile. The Wagner girl is therefore Jennifer. Frederick is therefore the Lee baby. Frederick is one of the two smallest babies (given), but does not weigh five pounds, fifteen ounces (since then Lucile Shirley, who has a different birthday from the smallest baby, would be the six-pound, seven-ounce baby and would thus be eight ounces heavier than Frederick Lee, which is contrary to what is given). Frederick is therefore the smallest baby, at five pounds, five ounces, and so was born on March 27. Jennifer by elimination was born on March 30.

The six-pound, seven-ounce baby was therefore born on April 2 (three days after the Wagner baby, as given), and is therefore Lucile Shirley. The five-pound, fifteen-ounce baby is therefore Jennifer.

In summary: Frederick Lee, 5 lb. 5 oz., was born on March 27. Jennifer Wagner, 5 lbs. 15 oz., was born on March 30. Lucile Shirley, 6 lbs. 7 oz., was born on April 2. Wolfgang Sartorius, 7 lbs. 8 oz., was born on April 4.

Stanwick at the Circus (page 246)

The whole show takes 150 minutes, and the other acts take 46 minutes, so these four acts take 104 minutes. This equals Carlo's time plus half of Carlo's time (for Bobo) plus one-third of Carlo's time (for Delpho) plus another third of Carlo's time (for Jilko, whose time equals that of Delpho). The 104 minutes therefore equals thirteen-sixths of Carlo's time, so Carlo's time is 48 minutes. Bobo's time is therefore 24 minutes, and Delpho and Jilko each need 16 minutes.

Jilko is third. Carlo is not first, last, or third, so he is second. Delpho follows Carlo, and so must be fourth. Bobo by elimination is first.